S0-AJD-089

REINHOLD PLASTICS APPLICATIONS SERIES

1. POLYETHYLENE

by

THEODORE O. J. KRESSER
Spencer Chemical Company
Orange, Texas

REINHOLD PUBLISHING CORPORATION
NEW YORK
CHAPMAN & HALL, LTD., LONDON

Library of Congress Catalog Card Number: 57-10348

REINHOLD PUBLISHING CORPORATION
Publishers of Chemical Engineering Catalog, Chemical Materials Catalog, "Automatic Control," "Materials in Design Engineering," "Progressive Architecture"; Advertising Management of the American Chemical Society

Printed in the U.S.A.

Reinhold Plastics Applications Series

No matter how remarkable the properties of a plastic may be, it is, after all, the most effective application of a material that counts. Many factors are involved in the determination of the optimum application. If, for instance, a certain plastic answers all the physical requirements for a particular end use, it still may not be the most desirable material for such use if another material which also will fulfill the physical specifications is available at a lower price. The most obvious properties of a material do not always determine its best application. Such minor characteristics as workability and processing odors may need to be taken into account in their effect on operating conditions, and certain intangibles such as color and feel may have an effect on consumer acceptance.

Realizing the importance of correct application in the whole gamut of plastics activity, the Reinhold Publishing Corporation in 1956 decided to publish a series of short books emphasizing the applications of the various types of commercial materials of the plastics industry—each book to cover one type of material. The present volume by Theodore Kresser is the first of this series. Others now in process cover the following types: acrylics, cellulosics, epoxies, fluorocarbons, laminates, polyamides, polyesters, polystyrenes, polyurethanes, gum plastics, silicones, and vinyls.

The series is semi-technical—that is, one does not need to be a chemist to understand the various volumes. The authors have kept in mind as probable readers such industrial men and women as: design engineers, equipment manufacturers, producers of packages, manufacturers of packaging machinery, students at technical schools and, of course, companies in the plastics industry—material manufacturers, molders, extruders, fabricators.

In addition to the above, it is hoped that each title will appeal to readers in specialized categories. Plastics from which fibers are made may be of interest to tire and fabric manufacturers. A book such as the one on vinyls, which materials are favorable for production of sheets, may have value for manufacturers of handbags and luggage. Similarly, other titles may appeal to manufacturers of paints, recorder tapes, upholstery, plywood and furniture.

With this program in prospect it is with enthusiasm that this book is presented.

HERBERT R. SIMONDS, *Editor*

Titles in Preparation

Acrylic Resins, *Nathaniel C. Ratner*

Cellulosics, *Walter Paist*

Epoxy Resins, *Irving Skeist*

Fluorocarbons, *Merritt A. Rudner*

Laminates, *Charles Nersig*

Polyamides, *Donald E. Floyd*

Polyesters, *D. G. Patterson*

Polystyrene, *R. R. Moyer*

Polyurethanes, *Bernard Dombrow*

Rubber with Plastics, *M. Stafford Thompson*

Silicones, *F. M. Lewis and R. N. Meals*

Vinyls, *W. Mayo Smith*

PREFACE

This book gives a brief summary of the status of polyethylene applications at present, with a little history and projection to bring it into reasonable perspective.

Without going into any great technical detail, I have tried to show how polyethylene is produced, and how it is made into useful articles. Since it is beyond the scope of such a book to describe any great proportion of the many applications of polyethylene, I have selected a few and tried to show the reasons why polyethylene was used for these purposes.

I have tried to keep in mind the needs of three groups of readers. The first of these is the general reader who knows little about plastics or polyethylene, but wants to get a general over-all picture of this remarkable new material. This reader must necessarily skim the book without worrying too much when he can't understand certain things. There will be many figures and formulas of no interest to him, but there are many pictures and descriptions which he will enjoy. The second group is the technical man with plastics experience, but no particular knowledge of polyethylene. This book will enable him to apply his previous knowledge to polyethylene in relation to other plastics. The detailed formulas and tables are mostly for him. The third group includes the business man, or technical man in fields other than plastics, who is interested in how polyethylene may be of value in his business.

Specific acknowledgment of the many sources cannot be made, since in many cases the ultimate origin of the data is not known. I have, however, mentioned as many as possible of the sources consulted directly, and illustrations are credited.

In compiling a book of this sort, the reliability of available data varies considerably, particularly in such a fast moving field.

No space has been given to ethylene polymers that are not plastic materials in the generally accepted sense, although many have been produced.

Orange, Texas
June, 1957

THEODORE O. J. KRESSER

ACKNOWLEDGMENT

The author wishes to express his appreciation for the unselfish way in which all segments of the polyethylene industry responded to requests for assistance in the preparation of this book.

Companies making a contribution included almost all major polyethylene producers, many makers of plastics processing machinery, and a large number of manufacturers of end use products. The list is simply too long to include. Some cases of specific indebtedness are acknowledged in the text, but in most cases data has been used from so many sources that exact acknowledgment is impossible.

Special thanks is due to the officers of the Spencer Chemical Company, whose decision made this project possible, and to the many Spencer people, especially among the advertising and secretarial staff, who took time from their regular duties to lend assistance.

So much of the material in the book was originally assembled by Mr. James Jordan and the Spencer market research group, that I feel obliged to make an exception to my rule of not mentioning individuals, and acknowledge my great indebtedness to him.

Orange, Texas THEODORE O. J. KRESSER

CONTENTS

1. INTRODUCTION AND HISTORY

It is commonly thought that the plastics industry is a new industry, and in the modern sense of synthetic plastics this is true. However, like so much of modern life, it has roots that go into remotest antiquity. In England, this tradition is well preserved in that one of the plastics industry organizations retains the name of "Society of Horners." The transparent plastic wrapping seen everywhere today is a direct descendant of the "Horn book" from which the children of colonial times learned to read.

Horn and tortoise shell are, in a sense, natural plastics, in that they can be softened in hot water and pressed into shape, returning to their original hard condition when dried out. Horn spoons and horn goblets show a remarkable similarity to their present plastic equivalents. The techniques developed to process the horn made it possible to use the newer materials as they were discovered.

Present day plastics fall into two general classes—thermoplastics which soften when heated and harden again when cooled, and which can be heated and cooled repeatedly, and thermosetting plastics which will melt and flow only once, becoming permanently set.

The thermosetting plastics are of great interest both historically and in their current development. One of these, phenol formaldehyde resin, known as "Bakelite" from the pioneer producer the Bakelite Corporation, was the earliest plastic to be commonly recognized. It was introduced in 1909. This type of resin still remains one of the greatest volume plastics produced. Some of the most dramatic and conspicuous modern developments like plastic boats and plastic automobile bodies are based on polyester resins; these are also classified as thermosetting because they cannot be softened again.

However, since the subject of this book is polyethylene, a thermoplastic, the development of thermoplastics will be covered without further discussion of thermosetting resins.

Unlike the development of thermosetting resins which started with purely synthetic resins, thermoplastics can be traced from the natural plastics such as horn and the natural resins such as shellac and copal through plastics which are based on modified natural products.

The use of bits of amber, too small to be of value by themselves, for molding under heat and pressure into various articles such as cigar holders is a very old art in the Baltic countries. The molds and techniques employed for this purpose are identical in principle to those used in compression molding thermoplastics today.

After the natural materials, the first thermoplastic was cellulose nitrate, which was given the trade name "Celluloid." It stemmed from a discovery made by Hyatt in 1868, the same Hyatt, incidentally, who invented the ball bearing, that cellulose, when nitrated and mixed with camphor made a strong, tough material that could be fabricated by methods similar to those used for horn and tortoise shell. He also found it possible to simulate many other natural materials in specific uses such as ivory in billiard balls and piano keys. Hyatt did a most remarkable job in exploring the potentials of this material and laid the foundation of the present thermoplastic technology. He borrowed equipment used in the rubber industry for producing his mixtures, and adapted techniques used both in the rubber industry and in the fabrication of the natural plastic materials. Since "Celluloid" also had properties not found in the earlier materials he developed new techniques to exploit these properties. The borrowed techniques included the use of the two-roll mill for compounding, the screw extruder or rubber "tuber" for the production of rod, tube and various profiles, the hydraulic press to shape the softened plastic, and such machine tools as the lathe, shaper, drill, planer, milling machine, etc., to shape the final product. New techniques which he developed were solvent cementing, press lamination, press polishing and embossing, and injection molding. Because of the thermal instability of cellulose nitrate the latter process was never a commercial success, but the principle is the current basis for one of the largest methods of producing articles from thermoplastic resins.

The high flammability of cellulose nitrate led to a search for a nonflammable substitute. Cellulose acetate was introduced in the thirties to fill this need, and it was the advent of this material that made possible the development of injection molding. Molding shops sprang up all over the country and a number of machine manufacturers attempted to perfect development of the injection molding machine. At first, cellulose acetate sheeting was made by the skived block technique which had been developed for cellulose nitrate, but the superior thermal stability of the material soon permitted the development of extrusion methods for its production.

The limitation of cellulose acetate plastic as to permanence and weather resistance produced a search through other cellulose derivatives that ultimately resulted in commercial production of acetate-butyrate mixed esters, ethyl cellulose, and cellulose propionate. The work on cellulosics was cut short, however, by the development of two truly synthetic thermoplastics—vinyl chloride and its modifications, and polystyrene.

Vinyl chloride, because of a thermal instability almost as

serious as that of cellulose nitrate, did not, at first, follow the typical thermoplastic pattern. Since the highly plasticized formulations gave the least processing trouble, vinyl chloride had its initial success in uses originally associated with the rubber rather than the plastics industry. It was rarely injection-molded; it was extruded mainly for hose and for insulation on wire and cable. The method most frequently used for producing sheet was calendering, a process previously used only for rubber compounds. The new markets for vinyl sheet led to an increase in the calendering capacity in the United States, and the more stringent requirements for machine control for vinyl compared with rubber demanded improvements in the calender and the techniques of its use.

The second outstanding synthetic thermoplastic, polystyrene, had been known and studied for a remarkably long time before it came into mass production. Ostromislenski had produced polystyrene as early as 1925 and had studied its properties. Small amounts had been made at very high costs for special electrical applications, and in the late thirties it was introduced as a general molding material at moderate prices.

The synthetic rubber program during World War II made available large quantities of low-cost styrene. This encouraged many chemical companies to install styrene polymerization facilities, and in the years immediately following the war polystyrene sprang up from a small specialty plastic to one of the leaders in the field.

The injection molding equipment that had been developed earlier for cellulosics proved highly adaptable to polystyrene. As a result of the low cost per pound and the low specific gravity of polystyrene, compared with its cellulosic equivalent, the injection molding industry experienced another tremendous expansion. The flood of polystyrene articles, particularly in the toy line, soon made "plastic" synonymous with "cheap and breakable" as far as the general public was concerned. The manufacturers countered this problem with the development of a wide variety of improved "high-impact" polystyrenes. Nevertheless, a good deal of dissatisfaction with the material persisted.

The events mentioned above were largely responsible for the development of the plastics industry in the late forties. The basic aspects were:

(1) Production equipment throughout the country had been increased enormously to accommodate the large output of polystyrene moldings, and vinyl extrusions, and calendered materials.

(2) Injection molding, extrusion, and calendering machinery had undergone extensive improvements.

(3) A considerable degree of dissatisfaction with the existing materials was evident.

In view of this, it becomes comprehensible how consumption of polyethylene could make the phenomenal rise from a small volume specialty in the late forties to a volume leader in the industry.

It would be very easy to say that polyethylene "had everything," and indeed such claims were made. Polyethylene certainly had serious limitations, but it also had a number of properties that made it extremely attractive. To the polystyrene molder beset by complaints about the brittleness of his products, it offered a material almost indestructible in everyday use, at a price not too much above that of his own material. To the vinyl extruder, fighting corrosion problems and encountering troubles due to plasticizer loss, plasticizer odor, or plasticizer migration, polyethylene was a material which contained no troublesome chlorine to corrode equipment, and which was permanently flexible without the use of a plasticizer. Limited experience had indicated that it molded at least fairly well, extruded quite easily, and once you got the hang of it, it could even be calendered to a reasonably good sheet.

In view of this, it is easy to understand why such a tremendous number of firms joined the rush for a part of the new "Wonder Plastic" in 1952 when the Federal court ruled that ICI would have to broaden its licensing policy. To the surprise of the conservative people the appetite for polyethylene proved to be almost as insatiable as had been estimated. Initial problems were rapidly solved and resin modifications quickly broadened the range of applications.

The next step in this fantastic story started with the announcement by Dr. K. Ziegler of the Max Planck Institute at Mulheim, Germany, in 1954, and of the Phillips Petroleum Company in 1955 that usable plastic ethylene polymers could be produced without the tremendous pressures required by the ICI process. When the availability of the processes for licenses was announced the rush was even greater than it had been in 1952. By the summer of 1956, before a single commercial plant was in production, a low-pressure polyethylene capacity had been planned to produce no less than 395,000,000 pounds a year—a production twice as large as that which had been attained by cellulose acetate in 1955 after 20 years of steady growth, and greater than the total 1955 production of polyethylene. This tremendous capacity was planned for a material that had only been tested in pilot plant quantities; it had never been tested to determine its true position in the market.

The projected use of low-pressure polyethylene was based on reasoning similar to that which had soundly predicted the market for the high-pressure type. Equipment and techniques in the plastic industry had reached new highs and here was a "new poly" that had everything the "old poly" lacked—mainly more rigidity.

Figure 1-1 shows the production figures for all thermoplastics, and for polyethylene.

There are several interesting things about Figure 1-1. First, it will be noted that the growth of polyethylene has taken a course similar to that of all thermoplastics—a relatively long period of slow growth followed by sudden expansion. It is also notable that the recent growth of polyethylene accounts for a large part of the growth of all thermoplastics. This does not mean that it is the only increasing component, but rather that the increase in other components does little more than compensate for losses in still others.

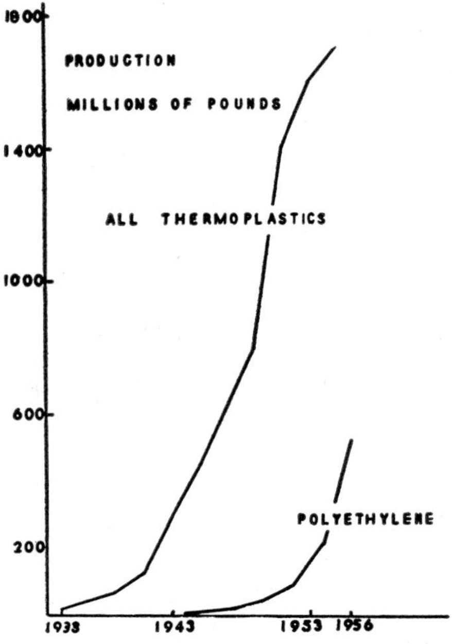

Figure 1–1. Production of all thermoplastics and polyethylene from 1933 to the present.

Polyethylene is unquestionably the principal growth factor in thermoplastics and increasingly its advance has been both at the expense of other thermoplastics and materials outside the plastics industry.

The introduction of polyethylene into the fields of other thermoplastics has been an important, but rarely mentioned, factor in the price cuts both in vinyl and polystyrene in recent years, in the face of generally increasing costs. The effect this competition in thermoplastics will have on the ability of polyethylene to maintain its rate of increase will be discussed in Chapter 9.

History of Technical Developments

By 1933 the use of the ethylene group in an organic chemical to produce giant molecules by addition polymerization was quite familiar to organic chemists.

The classic work of Ostromizlenski, Staudiniger and many others on styrene had established the nature of the reaction, and had also cleared up to some degree the reasons for the remarkable properties of the resulting products. As early as World War I the Germans had used the additive property of the ethylene group to produce synthetic elastomers on a commercial scale.

Despite the wide knowledge of the ability of the ethylene group to link long chains of molecules together for the production of high polymer molecules, ethylene itself had failed to yield true high polymers. Attempts at polymerization of ethylene had resulted only in oils and greases differing in no great way from natural aliphatic hydrocarbons.

In 1933 the British chemists Dr. E. W. Fawcett and Dr. R. O. Gibson were experimenting with ethylene gas at high pressure. They found that the introduction of small amounts of a catalytic material into the ethylene at very high pressure produced a rapid exothermic reaction which resulted in a tough thermoplastic resin which differed markedly from the soft waxy ethylene polymers previously produced. Analysis of the material proved that it was, in fact, an ethylene polymer of extremely high molecular weight. ICI obtained patents on this material as a new composition of matter.

Physical tests showed the polymer to have very interesting electrical properties, and on the basis of these properties the long and arduous work necessary to bring the reaction under control was undertaken.

It soon appeared that the combination of low loss, low dielectric constant, and high dielectric strength with toughness and flexibility made polyethylene the ideal dielectric for high frequency applications. Its usefulness in radar kept it reserved for this purpose for almost seven years.

Once the decision was made to develop polyethylene all the resources of the previously known polymer science and of the plastics and rubber industry were applied.

Despite the extreme conditions required for reaction, the ethylene polymerization was found to proceed by the free radical mechanism and to follow the same rules as known free radical polymerization of substituted ethylenes. Catalysts and inhibitors were borrowed from this science. Antioxidants were borrowed from the rubber industry. The resources of the chemical and petroleum industry were applied to provide a suitable source of pure ethylene gas. In a few years polyethylene went through all the stages of development that had taken decades with other polymers.

Commercial production was started by ICI at Northwich in Cheshire; the first ton was made in 1938 in pilot-plant equipment and in 1940 production was 100 tons. Toward the end of the war British production was roughly 1,500 tons a year.

The first application of polyethylene was by the Telegraph

Construction and Maintenance Company, in England, for the construction of submarine cable. It was used because of its low dielectric loss and great water resistance. In this instance it was compounded with polyisobutylene which made it more readily usable in the gutta-percha extruders available, although the added flexibility imparted by the polyisobutylene was also an advantage in this application. This was its only large-scale use until the war broke out, when polyethylene insulated cable for high frequency lines took on tremendous significance.

Polyethylene enabled the British to make extremely rapid progress in the radar field and there can be little question that it was a significant factor in the success of the "Battle of Britain."

In addition to the role it played in the radar field, polyethylene contributed greatly to the improved performance and durability of high-frequency communication cable; it was extensively used in army field wire at the end of World War II and during the Korean War.

The great military significance of polyethylene led the United States government to interest two corporations in its production. In 1943 the Bakelite Division of Union Carbide and Carbon Corporation and the DuPont Corporation obtained licenses from ICI for the production of polyethylene. With government assistance large production facilities were established and before the end of the war production in the United States exceeded that of the United Kingdom.

While the wartime development was based on the electrical properties of polyethylene, it had very quickly become evident that the material had other very valuable properties. These included the remarkable chemical inertness and moisture resistance to be expected of a hydrocarbon material, coupled with flexibility and impact resistance that were inherent properties of the resin, and not dependent upon the addition of plastizers as with other plastics. It was also found that the physical properties were much less temperature dependent than those of most other plastics, flexibility being maintained at very low temperatures.

Simultaneously it was found that polyethylene was remarkably adaptable to almost every method of plastic fabrication and processing known, and new applications developed so rapidly that even after wartime demands ended the material remained in short supply. The two original producers rapidly expanded their facilities without catching up with the demand.

One of the first applications outside the electrical field was for corrosion-proof construction in the chemical industry. Pioneer work in this field was done at American Agile. This company adapated the techniques developed in Germany for the fabrication of rigid vinyl chloride sheet to polyethylene. In this way they were able to produce fairly large fabrications which were used primarily for tank linings and ductwork. These were entirely resistant to corrosion by ordinary corrosive agents and were also found to have unusual resistance to degradation by radiation. In particular, polyethylene filled boron compounds have found wide application in the atomic energy field. The remarkable results obtained by radiation from an atomic pile were reported by Charlesby, Proceeding of the Royal Society 1952.

The application that requires the greatest amount of polyethlene in the United States at present is film. This is used predominantly for packaging although there are many other applications that may play a larger part in the future. The pioneer work was done by Visking. They developed a remarkable method of production that is feasible with a few other plastics but which appears to be particularly suitable to polyethylene. It will be described in detail later but is mentioned here because it represents the first large civilian use for polyethylene.

Before the development of film, the greatest part of polyethylene production was in some way related to national defense. Film was the first product that brought polyethylene into direct competition on the market, and its tremendous acceptance clearly demonstrated the value of the material. The remarkable water resistance of polyethylene had long interested people in its value as a barrier material.

It soon became evident that moisture resistance combined with considerable permeability to gases such as oxygen and carbon dioxide made polyethylene particularly adaptable to the packaging of fresh produce. The produce was prevented from drying out, yet the normal function of respiration was not prevented.

Polyethylene proved itself one of the best of the thermoplastics for injection molding. Pioneer in this field was the Tupper Corporation which placed injection molded polyethylene drinking glasses and numerous houseware items on the market during the 1940's, firmly establishing polyethylene in this field. The shortage of material prevented rapid expansion until about 1954, when it became more readily available and new grades especially adaptable to injection molding were introduced. The new materials, coupled with machinery developments, made possible the economical production of large moldings and a number of items like waste baskets and baby baths appeared on the market.

This rapid expansion brought out the fact that had hereto been hidden by the extremely easy adaptability of polyethylene. This was that, while polyethylene could be molded very easily on the conventional injection molding machines used for other thermoplastics, these machines were, in fact, poorly adapted to economical polyethylene molding.

This led to changes in molding machine design that will be discussed later.

In 1952 the United States Government obtained a court order instructing the ICI to offer licenses to other producers. At that time several concerns took out ICI licenses for the production of polyethylene. The first of the new producers was the Texas Eastman Company who went on stream late in 1954, followed in 1955 by Monsanto, Spencer, National Petrochemicals, Dow and Koppers.

About this same time a great deal of interest was aroused by the high-density ethylene polymers introduced by the Philips Petroleum Company and Ziegler in Germany. Although these showed some of the same properties as polyethylene they differed rather radically in general physical properties. In particular, they were a great deal stiffer and showed high heat distortion temperatures. These polymers are produced by solid catalysts capable of initiating polymerization under much more moderate conditions than those required by the ICI method.

The original belief that these catalysts would permit more economical production of polyethylene, and a drastic cut in price, has not yet been substantiated, as other problems appear to be keeping production costs up.

The remarkable properties of the polymers should broaden the field of polyethylene's usefulness. The future prospects of these materials and of standard polyethylene will be discussed more fully in Chapter 9.

2. GENERAL PROPERTIES

The applications of polyethylene are based on its properties. Sometimes a given application is based on a specific property, but more often an application is based on a combination of properties.

In simplest terms, polyethylene is popular for housewares and toys because it is unbreakable. It makes a good squeeze bottle because it is squeezable. It makes a good packaging film because it is cheap, tough, and moisture resistant. Yet these simple properties do not in themselves explain the tremendous expansion in polyethylene applications that has taken place recently. There are certainly many materials that could make a fine squeeze bottle, yet it is polyethylene that is being used—not some other material. This is because there is some combination of properties in each case that makes polyethylene outstanding. This chapter will attempt to bring together the combination of properties that makes polyethylene outstanding in each particular application.

While the earliest uses of polyethylene were based on its extraordinary electrical properties, the largest market today, film and pipe, is based on a combination of physical properties which at first glance do not appear to be outstanding. The figures commonly quoted on the resin for specification do little to reveal its special advantages. An attempt will be made therefore to discuss the characteristics of the products made from polyethylene rather than the properties of the resin itself.

The largest single market for polyethylene at present is for thin film, used primarily in packaging. Some understanding of the reasons for its wide use can be obtained from a study of Table 2-1, which indicates the large number of properties in which polyethylene film is as good as or better than competitive materials. There are also significant properties such as water vapor transmission in which polyethylene is inferior to other films, but still so good that the relative standing rarely has competitive importance. There also are other cases, such as oxygen transmission, where an apparent weakness can sometimes be turned into an advantage. This will be discussed later.

Availability is an important factor in considering any material for packaging. The large number of processors of polyethylene film makes it readily available in all parts of the country. Unlike most other films, it is available not only in film form, but also in the form of flat or gusseted tube in all dimensions. Almost every section has extruders equipped to manufacture any desired tube size, for the most economical packaging of an article. Establishments are also available for making bags out of the tubing, and for printing on it. In many cases, the tube manufacturer will also make bags.

Polyethylene film is made in greater widths than any other transparent packaging material, and the number of widths available is increasing constantly. This is of greater importance in the building trades than in most packaging, permitting applications not possible with other materials. The availability of extremely thin polyethylene film opens up new applications where the cost of other materials would be prohibitive.

TABLE 2–1. PROPERTIES OF SOME REPRESENTATIVE

General:				
Base material		Regenerated Cellulose	Lacquered Reg. Cellulose	Cellulose Acetate
Forms available	*	Sheets and rolls	Sheets and rolls	Sheets and rolls
Clarity		Transparent	Transparent	Transparent
Thickness, mils	*	0.8-1.6	0.9-1.7	0.5-2
Maximum width, in.	*	60	60	52
Yield (sq. in. of 1 mil film per pound)	*	21,500	19,500	22,000
Approx. specific gravity	*	1.45	1.40-1.55	1.25-1.35
Mechanical:				
Tensile strength, psi		4,000 18,000	4,000 18,000	5,000 12,000
Elongation, %	*	15-25	15-25	15-50
Tearing strength (Elmendorf) g/mil		2-10	2-10	2-15
Folding endurance	*	Fair	Fair	Fair
Heat sealing range, °F		Not sealable	200-300	350-450
Chemical:				
Water absorption in 24 hr. immersion test, %	*	45-115		8-10
Water vapor permeability—g/24 hr/100 sq. in. at 100°F, 90% relative humidity		Very high rate	0.2-1.0	100
Permeability to gases (O_2 and CO_2)		Dry—very low Moist—variable and higher		Medium
Resistance to alkalies	*	Poor to strong alkalies	Poor to strong alkalies	Poor to strong alkalies
Resistance to acids	*	Poor to strong acids	Poor to strong acids	Poor to strong acids
Resistance to greases and oils		Impermeable	Impermeable	Good
Resistance to solvents		Insoluble	Insoluble	Soluble, except in hydrocarbons
Permanence:				
Maximum use temperature, °F		300°F	300°F	200°F
Minimum use temperature, °F	*	Depends on type and R.H.		Becomes brittle
Resistance to sunlight	*	Good	Good	Good
Dimensional change at high RH, %	*	3-5	3-5	0.6% at 80%
Resistance to storage	*	Good	Good	Excellent
Flammability		Slow burning	Slow burning	Slow burning

* Polyethylene equal to or superior to other materials.

TRANSPARENT PACKAGING FILMS

Rubber Hydrochloride	Polyethylene	Polyvinylidene Copolymers	Vinyl Resins	PVC and Nitrile Rubber Blends
Continuous rolls and sheets	Rolls and sheets, flat tubing, gusseted tubing	seamless tubes, rolls	Rolls	Rolls, sheets and tubing
Transparent	Translucent	Transparent	Transparent to slightly hazy	
0.4-2.5	0.5-10	0.5-10	1-10	1-3
60	196	54	84	40
24,000	30,000	16,300	21,600	23,500
1.12-1.15	0.92	1.68	1.23-1.27	1.18
3,500 5,500	1,500 2,500	1,800 15,000	1,400 5,500	2,500 4,000
350-500	50-600	20-140	150-500	250-500
20-1,000	75-200	40	60-1000	300
Very high	Very high	Very high	Good	Very high
250-350	230-300		200-350	325-400
5	0.005	Negligible	Negligible	Very small
0.5-1.5	1.2	0.15	4-6.0	9.4
Low to high	High	Very low	Medium	Low
Good	Excellent	Good except NH_4OH	Good	Good
Good	Excellent	Excellent except H_2SO_4, HNO_3	Good	Good
Good	May swell	Excellent	Good	Excellent
Soluble in cyclic hydrocarbons and chlorinated solvents	Excellent, but may swell slightly	Excellent	Soluble in some	Soluble in some
200°F	180°F	200°F	200°F	200°F
—20°F	—60°F	—20°F	—50°F	32°F
Fair	Good	Good	Fair	Fair
Slight	None	None	None	None
Good in dark	Excellent	Good	Excellent	Excellent
Nonflammable	Slow burning	Self exting.	Slow burning	Slow burning

One of the most significant factors in the packaging field is its highly competitive nature. This lends added emphasis to the yield factor which, at current resin prices, makes polyethylene the cheapest transparent plastic packaging film available.

A short explanation of the yield factor may be desirable, since understanding it answers many questions about costs. This represents the square inches of film .001 inch thick that can be obtained from one pound of resin. The high value for polyethylene shows that more film of any given thickness can be made from a pound of polyethylene than from a pound of any other plastic. This results in a very low price for polyethylene films. (Table 2-2).

TABLE 2–2. PRICE COMPARISON BETWEEN POLYETHYLENE AND CELLOPHANE

Material	Cost/lb.	Yield, Sq. in. per lb.	Cost/1000 sq. in. 1 mil
Polyethylene (1.5 mil) (18 in. or wider)	$ .52	30,000	$ .018
Cellophane	$ .59	19,500	$ .030

(This is a basic price comparison, and does not take into account price variations among geographical areas, narrow widths, or additional costs such as printing or sealing.)

The tensile strength of polyethylene film is rather low, but it appears that service failures are rarely caused by tension alone. In practical use, polyethylene film is extremely durable. The high elongation, high tear strength, and great folding endurance are undoubtedly contributing factors.

Ease of heat sealing has been an important factor in the

acceptance of polyethylene film. The heat-sealing range shows that it is not outstanding in this respect, but it is still so good that it makes no practical difference.

The low-water absorption of polyethylene film prevents wrinkling and distortion due to changes in humidity, or in the presence of water drops, which mar so many other films.

The low-water vapor permeability of polyethylene is one of the principal reasons for its use. While there are less permeable films available, the permeability of polyethylene is so low that for most practical purposes, it is a complete barrier to water vapor. Hygroscopic materials can be stored in polyethylene bags for long periods under adverse conditions without damage, and moisture loss from wet materials is negligible. As a matter of fact, the water vapor resistance of polyethylene is too great for many uses such as packaging fresh produce, and the packages are perforated for ventilation.

The high permeability of polyethylene film to gases, especially oxygen and carbon dioxide, is sometimes a disadvantage while at other times it proves to be a distinct advantage.

One of the largest uses of polyethylene film is for packaging fresh produce where a combination of low-moisture transmission with high transmission of oxygen and carbon dioxide has proved to have a unique advantage. The deterioration of fresh produce is caused principally by moisture loss, yet in order to remain in good condition, most produce must be able to continue a degree of respiration. This means that it must have oxygen available, and be able to eliminate carbon dioxide. A completely impermeable container prevents respiration and the produce rapidly decomposes. Polyethylene has the unique ability to prevent moisture loss, yet to permit respiration.

A similar situation exists in the packaging of fresh meat where the presence of oxygen is needed to develop and maintain the attractive red "bloom" of the meat. A package completely impermeable to oxygen gives the meat a dull brownish color not associated with freshness.

The remarkable resistance of polyethylene to acids and alkalies, as well as to many other corrosive chemicals, has led to its use in packaging such materials. These applications do not generally use film alone. Small quantities are packaged in film, while film liners are used in other packages to fulfill the chemical resistant function.

Sometimes the relatively poor resistance of polyethylene to fats and oils is a disadvantage, while in many cases, such as meat wrapping, it has quite adequate resistance to the fat. The low maximum use temperature is also a limitation. However, polyethylenes considerably improved in this respect have appeared on the market. The resistance of polyethylene to sunlight and changes in humidity is extremely important in all applications, particularly packaging, since the polyethylene bag can be counted on to retain its strength and appearance over a reasonable period of storage.

A remarkable property of polyethylene film is the permanence of its physical properties. This is extremely important when it is used in building insulation. In applications where it is not exposed to sunlight it deteriorates very slowly, even if no particular effort is made to preserve it. Table 2-3 shows data on blown polyethylene film representing a span of about five years. It will be observed that the second test shows considerable improvement in practically all properties, probably due to the relaxation of some of the stresses produced during fabrication. Subsequent aging in most cases did not cause deterioration even to the extent of dropping the properties to the original values. From such data it is possible to project a long useful life for polyethylene films.

TABLE 2–3. EFFECT OF AGING ON TENSILE AND TEAR PROPERTIES OF POLYETHYLENE FILM

Property		Test 1 10/7/48	Test 2 1/26/50	Test 3 1/29/51	Test 4 8/10/53
Tensile strength, psi	MD	3624	3049	3563	3708
	TD	1419	1720	1799	1539
Elongation, %	MD	196	225	178	230
	TD	154	864	464	650
Tear strength g/mil	MD	153	228	250	196
	TD	109	108	119	80

Polyethylene Laminates and Coatings

Polyethylene is combined with other materials in two basically different structures. In coatings a layer of hot polyethylene is applied over another material forming one outer surface of the combination, and adhering to the base material by its own adhesive property. A laminate may be one of two other structures—a film of polyethylene made independently from the substrate and adhered to it with some sort of adhesive, or a combination of two webs joined by the use of polyethylene as an adhesive. This is mentioned because the terminology at present is somewhat confused and polyethylene coated papers are often referred to as laminates.

Coatings and laminates do not use as much polyethylene as free film, but these applications are growing very rapidly. In many cases it is possible to coat polyethylene to another material to obtain a combination of properties superior to either one.

The most widely used coating from a volume standpoint is polyethylene to Kraft paper. In this instance, the Kraft provides the strength the polyethylene lacks, while the polyethylene provides the moisture barrier lacking in the Kraft.

When polyethylene is used as the inner coating of a multiwall bag it also prevents contamination of the contents by fibers rubbed from the Kraft during handling. In the multiwall bag, polyethylene coated paper replaces other moisture barriers such as asphalt.

The polyethylene coated paper bag has shown a remarkable service record in comparison with asphalt waterproofed bags. It has been found possible* to substitute one wall of 15# (.001 inch) polyethylene on 50# Kraft for two walls of 30# Kraft, 30# asphalt, 30# Kraft. Five-year service records on over 20,000,000 bags showed that the bag with one polyethylene coated wall is equal to that with two asphalt coated walls in summer and better in winter. This bag holds 100# of product. Polyethylene coated bags are more flexible and easier to handle, and the over-all barrier properties are better.

This improved service life with polyethylene is not predictable by any laboratory test; the only test which gives a reasonable correlation of service is simply to drop the bag from an elevation a number of times until it fails.

One of the largest volume and most interesting coatings is cellophane coated polyethylene. These two films complement each other as regards permeability; polyethylene provides the moisture barrier while the cellophane is resistant to oily materials and gases. The polyethylene also acts as an adhesive giving the coated material heat-sealing properties.

Polyethylene-aluminum foil gives a high degree of impermeability and light opacity, while the polyethylene provides heat sealability and contributes to the impermeability by sealing the pinholes often found in thin aluminum foil. These laminates may also have a paper layer for added strength.

---

* K. A. Arnold, *Modern Plastics,* April 1956.

Polyethylene Monofilament

Polyethylene has the property of "necking in" on elongation. This property was first observed in nylon. When a thin rod of polyethylene, particularly of high molecular weight, is elongated it can be stretched out into a fine filament. Because of the molecular orientation which results from the stretching, the monofilament is a great deal stronger than normal polyethylene. Tensile strengths in the vicinity of 25,000 psi can be obtained. The oriented filament, of course, does not have the further ability to elongate a great deal, but it still is a very flexible material with adequate elongation for normal purposes. If heated the filament will shrink, and an annealing step is essential where this is undesirable. It is possible to keep shrinkage at normal use temperatures quite low when necessary. Some uses of polyethylene monofilament depend on the ability to shrink. Fabrics woven from polyethylene and other fibers can be given a useful three-dimensional effect by means of a heat treatment which shrinks the polyethylene filament.

The use of polyethylene monofilament in cordage is mainly based on the fact that it is the only cordage that will float permanently, which makes it useful in life-saving work; the permanent light color, which makes it easier to see, is also an advantage.

Polyethylene Pipe

The remarkable resistance of polyethylene to corrosion by water solutions of inorganic corrosive materials very quickly recommended its use in the chemical industry. The first polyethylene pipe was made for just such purposes. Tables 2-4 and 2-5 are partial lists of materials normally corrosive to metal piping that have little or no effect on polyethylene pipe. You will observe that this includes most of the common acids, bases and salts to very considerable concentrations at room temperature.

TABLE 2–4. SUBSTANCES CORROSIVE TO METALS BUT NOT AFFECTING POLYETHYLENE AT 60°C OR BELOW

Acetic acid, 10%			
Ammonia, dry gas or 0.88 sp. gr. solution			
Ammonium hydroxide, 28%			
Aluminum chloride	solution,	any	concentration
Ammonium sulfate	"	"	"
Calcium chloride	"	"	"
Calcium hypochlorite	"	"	"
Citric acid	"	"	"
Ferric chloride	"	"	"
Ferrous sulfate	"	"	"
Fluosilicic acid	"	"	"
Formic acid (100%)	"	"	"
Germanic tetrachloride	"	"	"
Hydrogen peroxide, 40 Vol.			
Hydrofluoric acid, 40%			
Lactic acid, 10-90%			
Magnesium chloride	solution,	any	concentration
Nickle sulfate	"	"	"
Nickle sulfite	"	"	"
Nitric acid, 10%			
Phosphoric acid, 30%			
Potassium hydroxide, 10%			
Potassium nitrate solution, any concentration			
Sea water			
Silver nitrate, 10%			
Sodium chloride solution, any concentration			
Sodium hydroxide, 10%			
Sodium sulfide solution, any concentration			
Sulfuric acid, 10%			
Tartaric acid, 10%			
Zinc chloride solution, any concentration			

TABLE 2–5. SUBSTANCES CORROSIVE TO METALS BUT NOT TO POLYETHYLENE AT ROOM TEMPERATURE

Chromic acid solution, any concentration
Fluorine, in water solution
Hydrogen peroxide, 100 Vol.
Hydrofluoric acid, 75%
Ozone
Phosphoric acid, 90%
Sulfuric acid, 50%

Engineers considering the use of polyethylene pipe must remember however that there are numerous chemicals that do attack polyethylene, particularly if the temperature goes above room temperature. Table 2-6 gives a partial list of materials which show an appreciable effect on polyethylene pipe. You will note that this list contains many hydrocarbons, particularly aromatics, also esters, ethers and ketones.

One group of materials that has a particularly subtle and dangerous corrosive action on polyethylene is the syndets. Many of these materials, even in relatively low concentration in water, will produce a type of failure in polyethylene pipe known as "stress cracking." The measurement of this property has received a great deal of attention and the polyethylene pipe now produced shows improved resistance to stress cracking.

The great volume of polyethylene pipe used does not depend on its chemical resistance. A closely related property, the insolubility of polyethylene in water, has proved advantageous in its use for potable water. In contrast to most metallic piping it adds nothing to the water in the way of contamination or off flavor.

However, the really significant properties responsible for its wide adoption in well and irrigation work are:

TABLE 2–6. SUBSTANCES ATTACKING POLYETHYLENE APPRECIABLY AT 20 AND 60°C

Substance	20°C	60°C
Acetic acid glacial	B	A
Acetone	A	A
Benzene	A	A
Bromine	A	A
Carbon disulfide	A	A
Carbon tetrachloride	A	A
Chlorine, dry gas	B	A
Chlorine, liquid	A	A
Chlorosulfonic acid	A	A
Cyclohexanone	A	A
Dibutyl phthalate	B	B
Ethyl alcohol	B	B
Ethyl acetate	A	A
Ethyl ether	A	A
Ethylene dichloride	A	A
Iodine (in KI solution)	B	A
Linseed oil	B	B
Lubrication oil	A	A
Methyl bromide	A	A
Methyl isobutyl ketone	A	A
Nitric acid, 70%, 95%	B	A
Oleic acid	B	A
Gasoline	A	A
Sulfuric acid, 98%	B	A
Toluene	A	A
Trichloroethylene	A	A
Xylene	A	A

A=Attack N=No Attack B=Borderline Cases

(1) Flexibility which permits coiling so that long lengths can be laid without coupling.

(2) Lightness which permits a man to carry considerable lengths.

(3) Easy installation, which has resulted from the development of simple and inexpensive techniques for joining.

(4) Price Table 2-7 shows that polyethylene pipe is one of the cheapest pipes available.

TABLE 2–7. COMPARISON OF PRICES OF PIPE PER FOOT

Material	½ in.	1½ in.	2 in.
Galvanized iron	$0.104	$0.305	$0.408
Black iron	0.087	0.253	0.338
Stainless steel	1.27	3.11	3.78
Copper tubing (type K)	0.270	0.915	1.34
Lead A A (water)	0.460	1.730	2.07
Aluminum	0.184	0.462	0.57
Brass	0.650	1.93	2.54
Butyrate (best)	0.190	0.57	0.73
Polyethylene (best)	0.140	0.467	0.600

Price comparison alone is not really significant because the cost of piping is the cost of the entire installation, not merely the pipe. In the average farm water installation, the farmer is able to install polyethylene pipe himself without special skills or tools, and it has been estimated that the cost of the entire installation is 30 per cent less than it would be with the cheapest metal pipe. Its ease of installation and low cost are responsible for the expansion of the polyethylene pipe industry.

Since polyethylene is a thermoplastic, temperature greatly affects the strength of the pipe, and if it is to be used at elevated temperatures this must be considered. Table 2-8 shows the effect of temperature on the burst pressure of polyethylene pipe.

TABLE 2–8

Test Temperature (°F)	Allowable Burst—Per Cent of 73.4°F Burst Pressure
60	110
65	105
73.4	100
80	95
90	80
100	70
110	60
120	50

As polyethylene resins of a higher density become available, it appears probable that the pressure and temperature limits of polyethylene pipe will be raised. Another factor which requires consideration is that the strength of polyethylene pipe is highly dependent on the way the pipe is made. Figure 2-1 shows the effect of extrusion temperature on the service life of polyethylene pipe. It can be seen that (1) pipe extruded at a low temperature is both weaker and more variable than that extruded at higher temperatures; (2) a warranty that pipe is made entirely of good resin, is no guarantee of service; if not handled properly a poor pipe can be made from a good resin. The importance of dealing only with the most reputable manufacturers when purchasing pipe is thus emphasized.

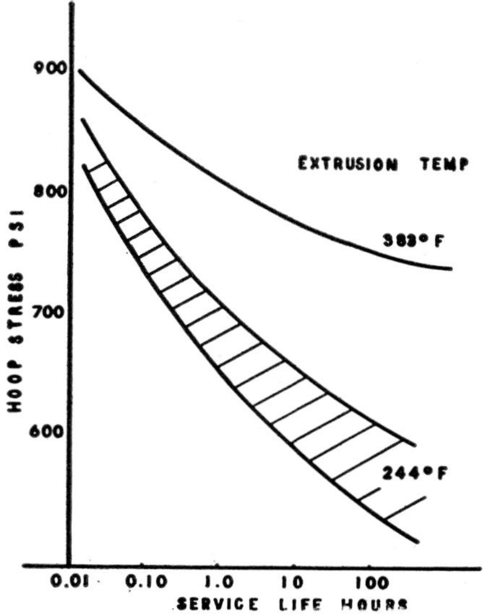

Figure 2–1. Effect of extrusion temperature on the service life of polyethylene pipe. (*Courtesy E. I. duPont de Nemours & Co.*)

Polyethylene Bottles

The polyethylene "squeeze bottle" is not only a container but also a method of dispensing the contents. The ability of this container to be squeezed, and then to return quickly to its original shape is significant in this application.

Also, the polyethylene bottle is unbreakable. These two factors—its usefulness as a dispenser and its unbreakability—are the properties that make polyethylene suitable for this application.

The problem of stress cracking mentioned previously is also important in the squeeze bottle. Special resins are commonly used to avoid stress cracking. The fact that many of the materials used in cosmetic formulations are rather readily transmitted through polyethylene proved to be a serious disadvantage at first. Some of these are shown in Table 2-9.

It was later found possible to coat the inside of polyethylene bottles with various materials that acted as barriers to these substances, thus extending the use of the squeeze bottle.

TABLE 2–9. GAS TRANSMISSION VALUES FOR POLYETHYLENE FILM AT 25°C

Gas	Transmission Value cc/100 sq. in./24 hr./mil
Nitrogen	180
Oxygen	550
Helium	1,225
"Freon 12"	1,690
Hydrogen	1,960
Carbon dioxide	2,900
Sulfur dioxide	6,200
Ethylene oxide	29,300
Methyl bromide	79,100

Modern Packaging, May 1954.

Figure 2-2 shows lined and unlined bottles containing carbon tetrachloride, a material rapidly lost through polyethylene. The unlined bottles collapsed in 24 hours, whereas the lined bottle is still full after 3 years. Polyethylene bottles are also used as chemical containers where chemical resistance is important. Here, they frequently replace glass containers on the basis of impact resistance.

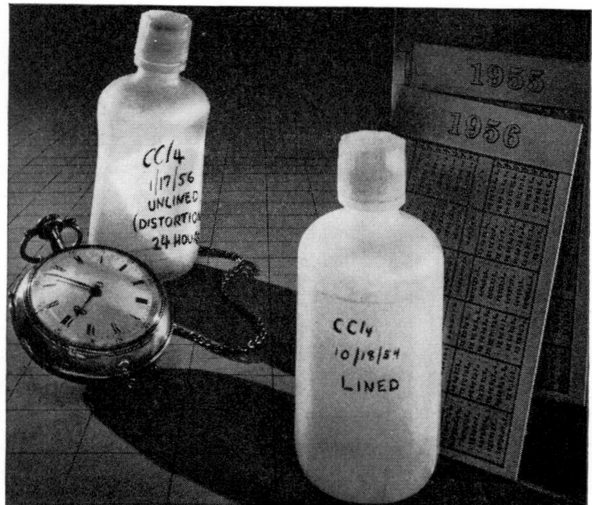

Figure 2–2. Effect of lining on permeability of polyethylene bottle.
(*Courtesy Plax Corp.*)

Polyethylene Collapsible Tubes

The properties significant in this application are similar to those affecting squeeze bottles. In contrast to metal tubes, these return to their original shape when released, thus preventing dribbling of the contents. They also retain their original appearance. Also many substances that attack metal, or which are contaminated by it, can be handled in polyethylene tubes.

Polyethylene Injection Moldings

The wide acceptance of polyethylene for injection molding has been based almost entirely on its toughness and flexibility. Polyethylene articles have proved to be virtually unbreakable in normal use. In addition to eliminating the fragility previously associated with the word "plastic," polyethylene articles retained certain advantages that had caused previous expansion in the field, such as unlimited color possibilities, all-through color, easy cleaning, light weight, and corrosion resistance. While polyethylene is slightly more expensive than competitive plastics the difference is more than offset by the unbreakability.

One special property of polyethylene housewares appeared with the large molding. Polyethylene containers are quieter than almost any other type. Making a loud noise when struck is largely a matter of modulus of elasticity, although the ability to absorb vibrations also is important. Polyethylene has both a low elastic modulus and a high ability to absorb vibration, making it a naturally quiet and quieting material.

In addition to the properties of the finished product, those which affect its fabrication are also important. The really big advance in polyethylene did not occur until easy flow resins were introduced. These resins made polyethylene one of the easiest of all thermoplastics to mold, especially extremely large pieces.

Polyethylene does, however, have certain properties that make it act differently in an injection machine than some of the more familiar plastics. Two of these are specific heat and thermal expansion. Polyethylene has a specific heat of 0.55 compared to 0.32 for polystyrene. This means that more heat has to be transferred to or from it for the same degree of heating or cooling. Although the thermal conductivity of polyethylene is appreciably higher than that of polystyrene, 8.0×0^{-4} cal/sec/sq cm/°C/cm versus 2.4-3.3 for styrene, the high specific heat puts a greater load on the heating cylinder of the machine and causes the part to hold its heat longer in the mold. Polyethylene therefore requires more mold cooling than polystyrene, and the capacity of the machine may be reduced when molding polyethylene.

The greater thermal expansion of polyethylene means that a part made from polyethylene will be smaller than one made in the same mold from polystyrene. Although the coefficients are 16 to 18×10^{-5} per °C for polyethylene versus $6 \times 8 \times 10^{-5}$ per °C for polystyrene, practical tests show a mold shrinkage ten to twenty times greater for polyethylene.

This greater mold shrinkage is due to a peculiarity of the flow behavior of polyethylene that is not easily described by a number. Plastic melts have a curious combination of properties that are partly liquid and partly solid. That is, they move in part by flowing like water, and in part by stretching like rubber; this rubbery part of the flow is always trying to recover a previous shape. In a rigid plastic like polystyrene, once it has hardened, the tendency to return is completely resisted. Polyethylene, however, is flexible enough even when cold to permit this "internal strain" to affect its shape somewhat. The high mold shrinkage is therefore not simple thermal contraction, but largely a "snap-back" like the contraction of a stretched rubber band. These figures are shown in Table 2-10.

TABLE 2–10. COMPARISON OF SOME PROPERTIES OF INTEREST IN INJECTION MOLDING

Property	Polyethylene	Polystyrene
Specific heat	0.55	0.32
Thermal conductivity 10^{-4} cal/sec./sq. cm./°C/cm.	8.0	2.4-3.3
Thermal expansion 10^{-5} per °C	16-18	6-8
Mold shrinkage in. per in.	0.02-0.05	.001 to .006

The low specific gravity of polyethylene has permitted it to compete with considerable success with cheaper materials.

Electrical Uses

The original use of polyethylene for insulating high-frequency cable depended on the electrical properties of the material. Table 2-11 lists representative electrical properties. The significant ones are the low power factor and the low dielectric constant.

TABLE 2–11

Property	ASTM Test Method	Units	Average Value
Water absorption	D 570-52	%	.01
Power factor	D 150-47 T	—	<.0003
Dielectric constant	D 150-47 T	—	2.3
Dielectric strength	D 149-44	volts/mil	850
Volume resistivity	D 257-52 T	ohm-cm.	>3 x 10^{15}
Surface resistivity	D 257-52 T	ohm-cm.	>4 x 10^{14}
Accelerated aging,			
IPCEA—IMSA Spec.			
Tensile strength		% Retention	90
Elongation		% Retention	90

However, as with all other applications, the utility and durability of the resulting article are the significant factors. Many properties contribute to these, particularly those shown in Table 2-12.

In most electrical applications the ultimate tensile strength of the insulation is not a major factor, but its flexibility is. Polyethylene shows remarkable flexibility in the sense of taking large strains without fractures and without excessive permanent deformation. It also is able to do this at extremely low temperatures, where even the elastomeric materials which are very flexible at ordinary temperatures tend to embrittle.

The extrusion properties of polyethylene are good and the equipment used for vinyl wire insulation can be used for polyethylene with some minor modifications.

TABLE 2–12. PROPERTIES OF POLYETHYLENE SIGNIFICANT IN ELECTRICAL WORK

Low water absorption
Low water transmission
High dielectric strength
High tensile strength
Light weight
Chemical inertness
Resistance to fungi and other organisms

Its adaptability to standard equipment has greatly facilitated the adoption of polyethylene in the wire industry by making it possible to run small amounts of polyethylene insulated wire in conjunction with the regular production of vinyl insulation, without making large investments in equipment. If the quantity warrants, more specialized equipment will evidently show greater efficiency.

In addition to the advantages polyethylene has for wire insulation some debits must also be considered of which the most serious are:

(1) Comparatively low temperature at which its characteristics deteriorate.

(2) Liability to injury by electrical discharges at its surface.

(3) High coefficient of thermal expansion.

(4) Liability to environmental cracking when stressed in contact with certain active agents, which include some commonly used lubricants such as metallic soaps and silicones.

(5) Liability to electrical failure under combined mechanical and electrical stress.

(6) Low resistance to termites, teredos, etc.

Since the communication industry has expensive and complex installations its requirements for a long service life are very stringent. For this reason, particularly for cable sheathing compounds, special emphasis has been put on the property of stress cracking, which appears to be the significant factor in service life.

Under complex stress, well below its ultimate tensile strength, polyethylene is subject to cracking. This can be greatly accelerated by stress-cracking agents, which include many of the popular syndets and silicone oils, as well as other surface-active materials. A similar effect, although probably caused by a different mechanism, is found with materials that have an appreciable swelling action on polyethylene, including most aromatic solvents, esters, ketones, and ethers. Many petroleum oils, such as transformer oils, also have this effect.

Figure 2-3 shows a sample of cable treated with "Igepal," an active stress-cracking agent. Numerical data showing the relation of stress-cracking to melt index are plotted in

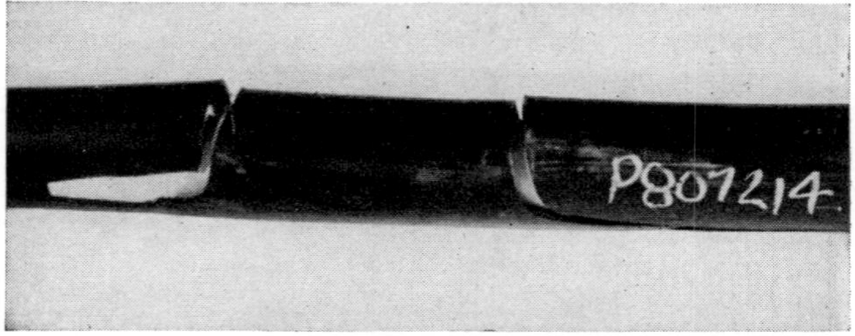

Figure 2–3. Sample of cable treated with "Igepal," an active stress-cracking agent.
(*Courtesy Bell Telephone Laboratories*)

Figure 2-4. These data would appear to indicate that the stress-cracking resistance is perfect at the 0.08 melt index level, but it merely indicates that the test is not extremely severe. This phenomenon can be found even at extremely high molecular weights but evidently approaches a level where it is no longer a significant source of service failures.

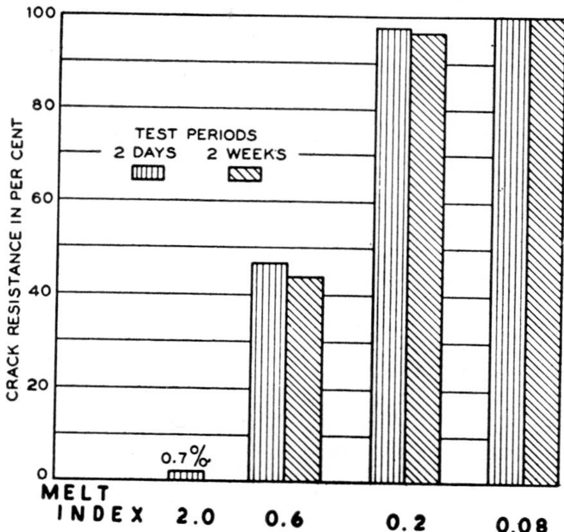

Figure 2–4. Relationship of stress-crack resistance to molecular weight.
(*Courtesy Bell Telephone Laboratories*)

Three terms have been used to describe the differences in the size of polyethylene molecules. In this discussion an increase in the Williams plastometer reading, or a decrease in melt index, is considered to be equivalent to an increase in molecular weight. Increased stress cracking resistance can also be obtained by compounding the polyethylene with

"Vistanex" or with "Butyl rubber." These terms will be discussed in detail in Chapter 3.

Table 2-13 is included to give some idea of the nature of environments that affect the strength of polyethylene. This gives the tensile breaking strain of an injected molded sample with a 1/16 inch drilled hole to produce a stress concentration in various environments. Such data has resulted in the use of special high-molecular weight, or low-melt index grades of polyethylene for cable sheathing. Low-melt index materials also show exceptional resistance to embrittlement at low temperatures, which is considered to correspond to service failure in some climates, and have improved abrasion resistance, which is significant for ease of installation.

TABLE 2–13. TENSILE BREAKING STRAIN OF INJECTION MOLDED POLYETHYLENE—NOMINAL VALUES OVER A 2-INCH GAUGE LENGTH, 1/16-INCH HOLE.

Sample	Air	Dist. Water	Soapy Water	Ethyl Alcohol	N Amyl Alcohol	+Amyl Alcohol	Toluene
1	51	60	51	18	6	7	14
2	62	54	41	38	15	13	18
3	39	42	46	36	20	20	14
4	45	45	51	44	25	20	21
5	42	44	44	40	29	26	20
6	48	47	47	44	36	38	38

(Cary ASTM Bulletin 167, July 1950)
These samples increase in molecular weight from 1 to 6.

Those materials that cause an appreciable loss of strength evidently are much more active on the lower molecular weight members of the series. Next to stress-cracking, temperature sensitivity is the main consideration limiting the use of polyethylene. The decrease in volume resistivity with temperature is given in Table 2-14, which shows a decrease in volume resistivity of several orders of magnitude in a rather short temperature range.

TABLE 2–14

	Volume Resistivity (ohm cm)	
	25°C	54°C
Unstabilized polyethylene	$1.2x10^{-9}$	$4.8x10^{-5}$
	$1.1x10^{-9}$	$4.1x10^{-5}$
Stabilized polyethylene	$1.7x10^{-8}$	$2.2x10^{-7}$
	$1.1x10^{-9}$	$2.0x10^{-7}$

Polyethylene contains dissolved air up to at least 10 per cent of its own volume when at equilibrium with the atmosphere. When heated it evolves gas at a relatively high rate but some of the gas is inevitably trapped during extrusion and tends to cause voids in the insulation. The presence of gas in these voids plays a part in the development of corona at high voltages. There is a decrease in the voltage required for the inception of corona with heat cycling; this can be reduced in part by proper cable construction but care must be taken that service voltages are kept below the corona point or rapid destruction of the cable will occur.

Although polyethylene is an extremely valuable material for wire and cable insulation, one of its main weaknesses has been its poor temperature resistance. Use of the higher density resins, with improved heat resistance, should extend the application of polyethylene in this field.

3. BASIC CHEMISTRY OF POLYETHYLENE

As indicated by its name, polyethylene is basically the polymer of ethylene produced by the reaction $N(C_2H_2) = (C_2H_2)n$ where N in the plastic grades is anywhere from 600 to 4000. It was originally believed that the polymer was essentially a straight chain composed by linking one polymer unit to another like a string of beads. Such a structure would have one terminal ethylene group per molecule and/or two methyls, depending on the position of the unsaturation. It soon became evident that commercial polyethylene differed quite appreciably from this theoretical model. For one thing, the chain ends per molecule were much greater than could be expected from this model. In 1940 Fox and Martin demonstrated, by infrared studies, the presence of at least one methyl group per 100 CH_2 groups. As infrared techniques have become more refined, two or three methyl groups per 100 CH_2 groups are commonly found.

A correspondingly higher degree of unsaturation can also be demonstrated by infrared techniques. This fact suggested that side branches can be formed during the polymerization, which evidently have a great effect on the properties of the polymer, particularly its ability to crystallize. Since the length of the side branches is also a significant factor, attempts have been made to estimate the proportion of long and short chains. The precision of the procedure used—which depends on reconciling measurements of methyl groups, of light scattering and of solution viscosities—leaves much to be desired, but it indicated a strong preponderance of short chains. The situation is made particularly difficult because there is no way to obtain a "known sample" from which to check the theoretical correlations. It is believed that five carbon side chains are the commonest, and that these are formed by transferring the active point at the end of the growing molecule back to the chain; this results in the break off of the original growing end as a branch, the chain continuing to grow at the new active point. The spatial configuration of the bonds on the carbon atom would favor this occurring at about 5 carbon atoms.

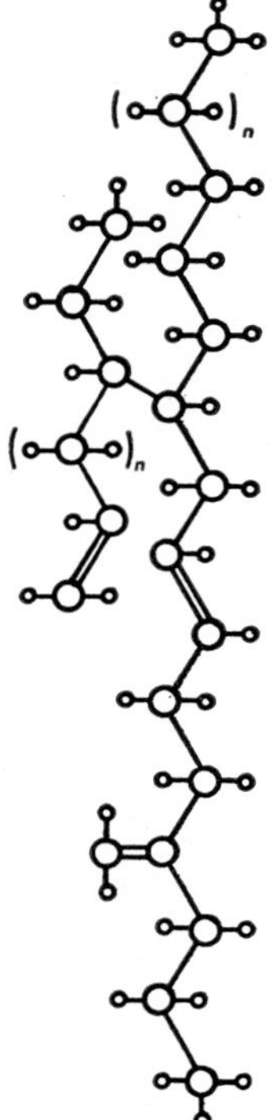

Figure 3–1. Polyethylene molecule showing some characteristic structures. Large circles represent carbon atoms; small circles, hydrogen atoms; double lines represent double bonds.

In addition to the extra methyl groups, investigators have shown the existence of three distinct types of unsaturation, a terminal double bond $RCH{=}CH_2$, a pendant double bond $RR'C{=}CH_2$, and a chain double bond $R{-}CH{=}CH{-}R$. Furthermore, a certain amount of oxygen is present in most polyethylene, probably in the form of carbonyl or keto groups.

Figure 3-1 is a simplified diagram of a section of a polyethylene molecule showing most of the structure discussed. No plane diagram can give any indication of the spatial complexities resulting from the tetrahedral orientation of the bonds on the carbon atom, but evidently this causes spiral and zig zag shapes.

The average molecular weight was the first factor brought under control to have any effect on the properties of polyethylene. As could be expected, when the size of the polymer increased, an increase in strength and in other properties occurred. This permitted the production of various grades of polyethylene adaptable to different purposes. It was soon found that average molecular weight did not entirely determine the properties of the polymer, and control of the molecular weight distribution was attempted. The relationship of polymer size to various properties is shown in Table 3-1.

TABLE 3–1. MOLECULAR WEIGHT DECREASE
OR
MELT INDEX INCREASE

To Get	Sacrifice
Easy flow	Stress crack resistance
Surface gloss	Tensile strength
Draw of film	Yield strength
	Tear strength
	Slip of film

Determining the molecular weight of any high polymer requires techniques radically different from the classical methods used for this purpose. Since the polymer cannot be gasified without decomposition the molecular volume cannot be determined. The reaction of groups within the molecule with a reagent requires exact knowledge of the structure of the molecule. The previous discussion has shown that the structure of polyethylene is by no means simple enough for this technique to give any reliable results.

These facts have caused molecular weight determination of high polymers to be limited to certain characteristics of solutions of the polymer. A polymer solution in an ultracentrifuge will stratify into layers depending on the size of the molecules. However, the expensive equipment and refined techniques required by this method have limited its use. It has as yet yielded little data on polyethylene due to the formation of agglomerates. In the case of polyethylene, the problem is complicated by the fact that solution can only be obtained at high temperatures, which makes it more difficult to control the temperature and carry out the operation.

The solution characteristics used to determine molecular weight are:

(1) Boiling point raising
(2) Osmotic pressure
(3) Freezing point lowering
(4) Viscosity
(5) Light scattering.

Of these, only the first three can be considered absolute methods; the others are merely empirical. For this reason, the first three must be used as a starting point in any molecular weight study. Formidable obstacles present themselves in all methods.

The boiling point increase due to the presence of high-molecular weight polyethylene is extremely small. The problem is particularly difficult because solutions of any considerable concentration are very viscous and do not boil normally. Extremely sensitive means have been devised for comparing the boiling temperature of a solution with that of the solvent. By measuring the differential temperature directly, the uncertainty of the absolute values is eliminated and meaningful measurements can be made. In spite of these refinements, it is better to limit this method to the lower range of ethylene polymers, as results obtained with polyethylene in the plastic range have been unsatisfactory.

When the solution of a polymer is separated from some of the pure solvent by a membrane permeable to the solvent but not to the polymer, the solvent will pass through the membrane until a pressure has been built up on the solution side sufficient to balance this tendency. This pressure is called the "osmotic pressure," and at a given concentration it decreases as the size of the molecule increases.

In this case, the necessity of working with polyethylene solutions at relatively high temperatures has proved a serious obstacle. The semipermeable membrane is sensitive and not too reliable even at room temperature, and at elevated temperatures it has given much trouble. It is, however, the only method reasonably reliable with molecules of a size in the plastic range and the best idea of the size of these molecules comes from this method.

The sources of trouble are deterioration of the membrane at the high temperature and back diffusion of the smaller polymer molecules through the pores of the membrane. These require that techniques be used to determine the equilibrium pressure very rapidly. Results using different solvents often disagree, apparently as a result of incomplete separation of molecules in solution, as with sedimentation methods.

It is interesting to note that these two methods are in a

sense complementary in that errors in the boiling point method will give low values for molecular weight whereas errors in the other methods will give higher values. If the methods agree reasonably well, a fair degree of accuracy can be assumed.

Freezing point lowering is another of the classic or "absolute" methods used in the determination of molecular weight. Like the boiling point raising method, its use on extremely large molecules requires the determination of extremely small temperature differences. Recent techniques have made it possible to obtain meaningful results by this method. However, the techniques are extremely difficult and are practiced in only a few laboratories.

In order to see how solution viscosity can measure molecular weight the mechanism by which a polymer molecule increases the viscosity of a solvent must be considered. This mechanism is a purely thermodynamic one. When the solvent flows, the polymer molecule is long enough to be in sections of the flow traveling at different rates. This causes the molecule to slip through the solution, creating heat and removing energy from the flow. The amount of slip depends on the size of the molecule, but not as much on its weight as on its length.

A great deal of work has been done to demonstrate the validity of the relation: $(\eta)_0 = K \frac{L^3}{\bar{M}}$

where $(\eta)_0$ is the intrinsic viscosity

K is a constant

L is the average length of chain (this represents the straight line distance between the chain ends, regardless of the location of other parts of the chain).

$\bar{M}$ is the molecular weight of the polymer.

This relationship holds for a wide variety of polymers.

Thus it is evident that unless the relationship of L to $\bar{M}$

is constant, viscosity cannot determine molecular weight. Since branching of the molecule obviously affects the length of a molecule of any given weight, the relationship of L to $\bar{M}$ cannot be the same for polyethylene resins which vary in branching.

Empirical equations have been worked out having the form $(\eta)_0 = K\ \bar{M}_n^a$ which are widely used to determine the molecular weight of polyethylene.

A comparison of this equation with the previous one shows how the shape of the molecule can introduce errors. In order to simplify this type of equation the natural logarithm of the intrinsic viscosity, often called "Logarithmic Viscosity number," can be used to eliminate the exponent.

For routine determinations it is common practice to make a single determination of viscosity at a rather low concentration, and use the relative viscosity, without the extrapolation to zero concentration.

It should be stressed that however calculated this is an entirely empirical relationship and the constants hold only for polyethylenes that are identical, except for molecular size, with those used to determine the constants. Using constants determined with polyethylene of one molecular weight distribution, or density, or degree of branching to determine the molecular weight of a sample of polyethylene differing in any of these respects, is an abuse of the method and makes no more sense than reporting the reading on a yardstick in meters. This is pointed out only because this abuse is very common and is sometimes cited to discredit this method of molecular weight determination, whereas it merely demonstrates a lack of understanding of the method.

For many years one producer reported the molecular weight of polyethylene merely as intrinsic viscosity X20,000 on the basis of work on solution viscosities of lower molecular weight paraffin. Data based on this relation are still frequently found in the literature and some data in this book include molecular weights so determined.

The viscosity method is one of the most popular ways for determining high polymer average molecular weight. It is easy to perform, reliable, and does not require expensive equipment. In the case of polyethylene, the problem is complicated because solvents cannot be used at room temperature and the operation has to be performed at elevated temperature, but this is not particularly serious in the case of viscosity measurements.

The light-scattering techniques depend on the fact that the polymer molecules, while invisible, are still large enough to cause an appreciable scattering of light as it passes through the solution. This technique actually measures the mean radius of the molecule in solution. Since the space occupied by the molecule may contain 10,000 times as much solvent as it does polymer, it is evident that this measurement cannot have a very specific relationship to the weight of the molecule. In particular, variation in branching will change the volume occupied by a molecule of the same weight, and as a result the radius measured by the light scattering. Under carefully controlled conditions light scattering can be correlated to molecular size, but like viscosity it does not measure weight directly.

Another optical method of measuring polymer size is flow birefringence. This is based on the fact that most polymer molecules are optically anisentropic. When a polymer solution is put in a shear field the molecules tend to orient, causing birefringence. This can be measured and related empirically to molecular weight.

Molecular size can be controlled in a routine way by determining the melt viscosity in an apparatus called the Melt Indexer. This will be discussed further under resin manufacture.

Another simple empirical method of approaching the molecular weight determination is called the ZST or zero strength time method. In this test a small notched sample is held under light load while the temperature is increased at a carefully controlled rate. The time it takes for the sample to break is related to the molecular weight of the sample, the higher molecular weights taking the longer time. This evidently depends on calibration of the apparatus with samples of known molecular weight, and many factors other than molecular weight enter into the ZST. It is useful for routine comparison of polyethylene known to be similar in all respects other than molecular weight.

In order to obtain molecular weight distribution a good fractionation procedure is necessary as well as a method of determining the molecular weight of the fractions. The commonest fractionation procedure is based on solubility. The longer molecules, having more secondary forces to hold them together, are slightly less soluble than the shorter chains. This difference is so small that very accurate temperature control is needed. Since the difference in specific gravity between the solution and the polymer is slight, long settling times are required for separation. The fractions produced by a single precipitation are by no means uniform; they have a slightly narrower distribution than the original polymer. A really narrow cut requires repeated resolution and reprecipitation, which makes it complicated and difficult to obtain a molecular weight distribution curve.

It is interesting that precipitates produced in fractionating polyethylene are relatively hard, permitting separation by filtration, in marked contrast to the soft slimes produced in fractionating other high polymers.

One attempt to characterize molecular weight range, without actually determining it, is based on the difference between the molecular weights determined by the various methods.

The main classical methods—boiling point raising, freezing point lowering, and osmotic pressure—are essentially means of counting molecules; average molecular weights determined in this manner are ordinary number averages—the total weight of all molecules, divided by their number.

The light-scattering technique, however, produces an average where the larger molecules have a much greater effect. The increase in effect of the larger molecules is approximately proportional to their size, so that the average obtained from the light-scattering technique can be approximated to a weight average. The weight average is the weight of molecules of one size, times their weight, plus the weight of molecules of each size, times their respective weights, the final sum divided by the weight of all the molecules. The weight average is always larger than the number average, except where all the molecules are identical, in which case it is the same. The ratio of weight average to number average gives a measure of the width of the distribution of molecular weight. A large ratio means a wide distribution; a small ratio means a narrow distribution. This ratio has been useful in studying the effect of molecular weight distribution.

Flow birefringence also tends to give higher molecular weight figures, presumably approximating weight averages, but these values do not appear to be identical with the light-scattering figures.

Despite the problem of determining molecular weight distribution, its control has been a major objective in polyethylene technology. Determinations have been made on polymers produced so as to show major differences in their molecular weight distribution. A good deal of information has been obtained from these determinations on the effect of molecular weight distribution on polymer properties, some of which are shown in Table 3-2. To a certain extent a narrowing of the molecular weight distribution has effects on polymer properties similar to an increase in the average molecular weight, or melt index. (Compare Table 3-1, page 42.) This has created a great deal of confusion since the melt index is commonly reported, whereas the molecular weight distribution cannot generally be determined. Since the molecular weight distribution of various commercial polymers varies a great deal it is frequently found that in order to get similar properties in the various resins, different melt indexes must be used.

TABLE 3–2. REDUCING MOLECULAR WEIGHT RANGE
OR
MELT INDEX RANGE NARROWING

To Get	Sacrifice
Film impact strength	Processability
Tensile strength	
Low brittleness temperature	
High vicat point	
Stress crack resistance	

The classic report of Carothers on the high molecular weight polyamides, published just before the discovery of polyethylene, had a great influence on the thinking of early investigators. He related the property of "necking down" on elongation—which forms an extremely strong, oriented fiber or filament—to a molecular size of about 1000Å and to the ability to crystallize. Polyethylene shows this property as well as a degree of crystallinity. The investigation of crystallinity revealed many interesting facts. For one thing, polyethylene is composed of crystalline areas surrounded by amorphous materials. The crystallites form about 60 per cent of the normal polyethylene, although estimates vary from 40 to 75 per cent, depending on the method used. One of the early studies on this subject was made in 1949 by Buckley, Cross and Ray who examined polymethylenes made from diazomethane by the method of Leitch and Cambron. This method of synthesis presumably does not provide any way for chain branches to form, and the resulting polymers showed negligible methyl groups in the infrared spectrograph. It can therefore be inferred that they are in fact the straight chain analogs of polyethylene. These materials differed radically from polyethylene in several respects. Their specific gravity is higher, they are almost completely crystalline, and they are hard horny materials without any of the flexibility shown by polyethylene. The crystal structure of polyethylene has been determined. The unit cell has the orthorhombic space group, Pnam, with a_0 equals 7.40 Å, b_0 4.93 Å and c_0 2.534 Å. The diffuse character of the X-ray pattern has been interpreted as being due to crystallite sizes between 100 and 300Å.

One of the most interesting findings of the study of the crystalline behavior of polyethylene is that the dimensions of the crystallites are so small under some conditions that it must be assumed that a single molecule is longer than the longest dimension of the crystallite. This means that one molecule may form part of a crystal and also part of the amorphous material surrounding the crystal. This is not difficult to understand in view of the mechanical difficulty of two long chains arranging themselves in such a manner as to crystallize; sooner or later a wrinkle or tuck will appear in one or the other, preventing further crystallization. This property, however, changes the relationship between the crystalline and amorphous phases from that found in more familiar materials such as metals. In the more familiar cases, the crystalline and amorphous phases are essentially separate entities joined only by normal cohesive forces, and often differing considerably in composition. In polyethylene, crystallite and amorphous material are identical. By analogy with inorganic crystals the word "crystal" suggests straight lines and accurate angles of polyethylene molecules lined up like logs on a raft, in a straight and orderly arrangement. The configuration of the polyethylene molecule will show how impossible this picture is. Even a "straight chain" without branches will never take on the shape of a straight line. The four bonds of the carbon atom, in consequence of their natural electrical repulsion try to stay as far apart as possible. This means that their relaxed position, to which they will always return when unstressed, can be represented by the four points of a tetrahedron. An attempt to connect the points of tetrahedra to form a straight chain will quickly show that any time a straight line results in one plane there is an angle in another. Two chains can crystallize together only by "mating" in tortuous spirals or zig zag patterns. The polyethylene crystal can more nearly be likened to a well entangled mass of fine springs, or to a tightly rolled ball of numerous ends of yarns, than to a raft of logs.

The arrangement of crystallite and amorphous regions in unoriented polyethylene is not a random one. The crystallites tend to form roughly spherical aggregates known as spherulites. The size of these spherulites varies from sub-microscopic to a few tenths of a millimeter. It is because of this tendency of the crystallites to grow radially from a point into spherulites that polyethylene appears translucent, and differences in transparency are more nearly related to spherulite size than to degree of crystallity. Recent work has suggested that there is a spiral arrangement of both crystalline and amorphous material within the spherulites.

Considerable work has been done to influence the crystallinity of polyethylene. The various techniques used to control crystallinity in metals or glass have remarkably little effect on polyethylene. Shock cooling a melt will result in a slightly clearer solid, but within a relatively short time it will be found to have almost the same degree of crystallinity as a piece cooled more gradually. Extremely slow cooling or annealing at rather high temperature may induce a slightly higher degree of crystallinity and very appreciable differences in properties, particularly in certain density ranges. This fact is made use of in some test procedures where the severity of the test can be influenced to a considerable degree by the preparation of the sample. Any test involving elongation is made more severe by sample preparation that induces maximum crystallization, for reasons that will become obvious later when the effect of density is discussed in detail.

Generally speaking, however, it can be said that no useful change can be made in the crystallization of polyethylene after the polymer has been produced.

Since increased crystallinity gave promise of improving the polymer in certain respects such as rigidity and tensile strength, a great deal of work was done to change the polymer molecule to make it inherently more crystallizable.

The early work of Buckley, Cross and Ray pointed the way toward a more crystallizable polyethylene by eliminating the chain branching. Their work did not, unfortunately, indicate a practical way to do it. It has been found that some degree of control over branching can be achieved in the high pressure method for polymerizing polyethylene by selecting the catalyst and by adding various modifying agents to the ethylene. This procedure is under development and it appears likely that it will ultimately be possible to make polyethylene of almost any density by the high-pressure method.

The much discussed low-pressure methods for polymerizing ethylene are techniques for achieving the same results. They are extremely versatile and when they are fully understood they should be capable of controlling not merely average density or degree of crystallization, but the fine detail of molecular configuration as well. These systems have in common the use of a solvent for ethylene which is not a solvent for the polymer, and the use of a catalyst that is insoluble in the solvent. The catalyst can be likened to a gateway between the solvent or ethylene phase and the insoluble polyethylene phase. The catalyst, then, is the only place where the active or growing end of the chain can contact supplies of ethylene for further growth. This means that different catalysts will be able to direct this growth in various ways, and result in different molecular configurations. It appears at present that these developments constitute a major break in our knowledge of molecular synthesis.

The following discussion on density relates to data too new to have had critical evaluation. The materials used as a basis for the graphs may have had significant differences other than density, but it is believed that density was the principal one. The actual numerical values cannot be taken very seriously but the general trends are believed to be valid.

Table 3-3 shows some effects of density increase on polyethylene.

TABLE 3–3. DENSITY INCREASE

To Get	Sacrifice
Increased stiffness	Elmendorf tear strength
Increased yield strength	Film impact strength
Increased ultimate strength	Film flex life
Creep resistance	Mold shrinkage increases
High vicat softening temperature	Stress crack resistance decreases
Impermeability to liquids and gases	"After shrinkage" increases

One of the most remarkable effects of density increase is the change in the shape of the stress strain curve. Figure 3-2 shows comparative stress-strain curves.

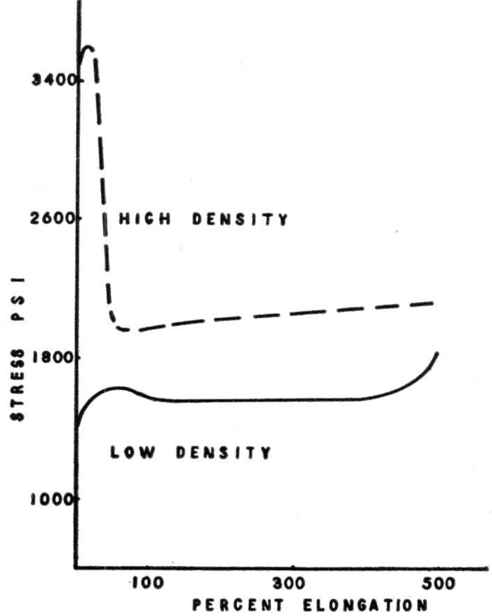

Figure 3–2. Change in stress-strain curve between low density and high density polyethylene. High density material has a tendency to fail at the yield point and will only complete the curve at low rates of strain.

The remarkable thing is that yield strength increases all out of proportion to tensile strength and to the stress required for cold draw. This makes a great deal of difference in how the material acts. For one thing the high density material, when the rate of strain is high, is inclined to break at the yield point, instead of elongating as low density material does. For some applications, however, elongation beyond the yield point represents failure of the piece anyway, so in these cases the loss is not serious. By having three important characteristics to manipulate, it is obvious that an almost infinite series of combinations and permutations exists. Depending on which property is most important, a different polyethylene can be made to suit each application.

One remarkable thing that does not stand out in these charts, because it is a negative fact, is that the density has little or no effect on the flow properties of the polymer, but a very large effect on the properties of the product. Unlike common plasticized thermoplastics it is not necessary to make a "soft" product in order to get a "soft" flow.

The "after-shrinkage" item in Table 3-3 requires some explanation. When a polyethylene melt first solidifies, it does not immediately reach its final density. The rate at which it crystallizes is somewhat dependent on the conditions of use, and can be controlled to some extent in making the polymer. However, this increase in crystallinity and density goes on for a long time, probably to some extent for the life of the product. This is necessarily accompanied by a decrease in volume or shrinkage. As the final density of the product increases, of course, the total amount of this shrinkage

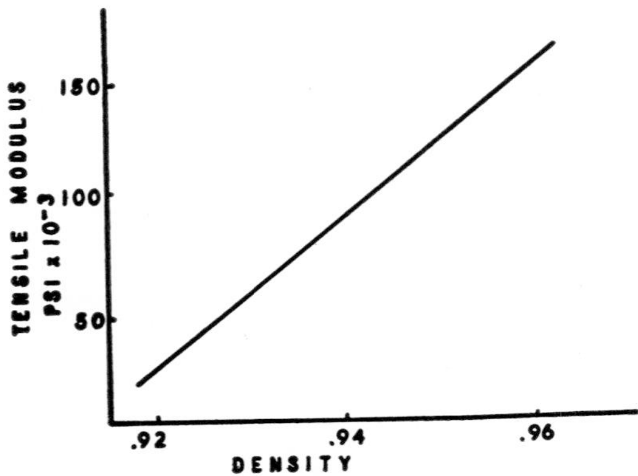

Figure 3–3. Change of tensile modulus with density.

increases. As the density increases, the elastic modulus also increases, hence the same amount of shrinkage creates much higher stresses in the high density polymer, adding to the problem of shrinkage. Because of the tendency of the high-density polymer to break under some conditions, at its yield point, rather than to elongate, there is a cracking problem with high density materials, especially in applications like wire insulating, where the plastic is mechanically prevented from shrinking. The possibility that this problem can be alleviated by controlling the molecular configuration is under intensive investigation.

The relationship between the density and many of the physical properties of polyethylene is a simple one; that is, a given increment of density gives the same change in physical property wherever it may lie. This is clearly illustrated by Figure 3-3 which shows a linear change in tensile modulus with density. Figure 3-4 shows the relationship between yield strength and density; this increases geometrically with density.

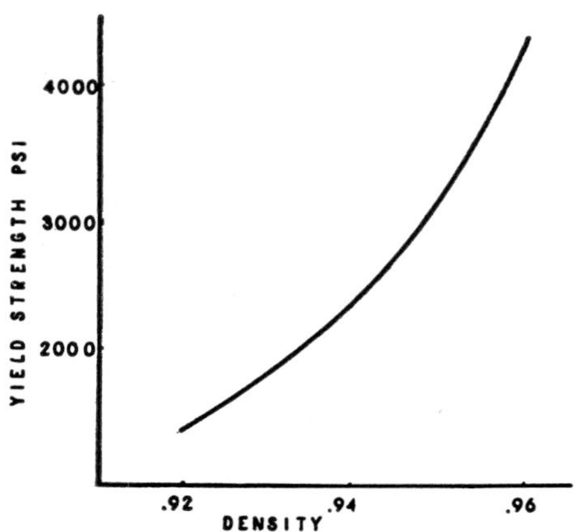

Figure 3–4. Change of yield strength with density.

There are other properties where a very sudden and drastic change occurs in one specific density range so that it can fairly be said that the material below this range is entirely different from the one above it. The most striking and significant property in this class is the ultimate elongation. When a tensile test is made at the 20 inch per minute strain rate, which is standard for this test (ASTM d412-51T), there is very little difference in elongation between a density of .92 and .93. However, above .93 there is a rapid decrease in elongation as shown in Figure 3-5 and by .95 the elongation is down to about 25 per cent or about 5 per cent of what it was at .93, above which it again changes little. It should be pointed out that this rapid transition in elongation is not an absolute transition point but, like most other relationships between physical properties, is in part an artifact of the test method. If the rate of elongation is decreased enough it is possible to get high elongation even on high density resins. Like all standard test methods this one has developed through years of experience and correlates well with practical use. That is to say, this rather arbitrary transition point corresponds to an empirical change from a soft ductile material to a hard and rigid one.

There have been some indications that at the same melt index, resins of higher density are lower in molecular weight. This is partly due to observations of physical properties thought to be a molecular weight dependent such as stress cracking. To obtain the same general level of values in the Bell Laboratories stress crack test it is necessary to use a lower melt index as the density increases. Izod impact results show a similar trend. Polyethylene with a density of .918 will not break in the Izod test until a melt index above 50 is reached. At .925 the limiting melt index is in the region of 20, while at .935 breaks are obtained at a melt index as low as 6. A smaller percentage increase in strength when a

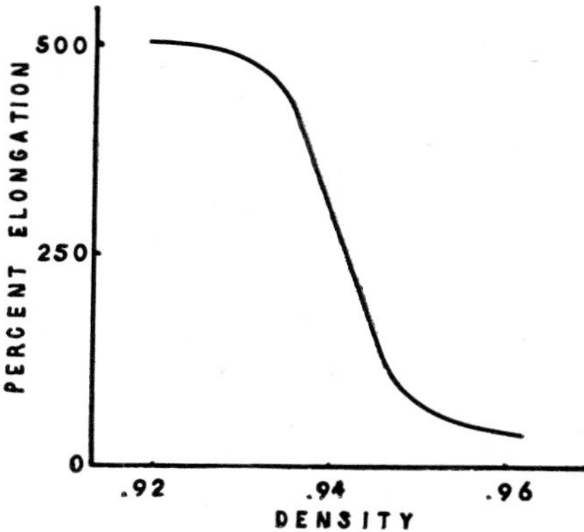

Figure 3–5. Change of ultimate elongation with density.
Strain rate 20 inches per minute.

filament of high density polyethylene is drawn has also been interpreted as indicating lower molecular weight. Evidently all these phenomena also have alternative explanations, as does the following basis for attributing lower molecular weights to high density materials than to lower density materials of similar melt index. The solution viscosity of a high density material is lower than that of a low density polyethylene of the same melt index. To workers using solution viscosity to determine molecular weight this means lower molecular weight. The pitfalls of this assumption have been discussed. The solution viscosity bears a relation to molecular weight that is dependent on an empirical factor related to molecular shape and solvation. Since the main difference between polyethylene of high and low density is molecular shape, and since the solubility of high-density polyethylene, so presumably its solvation in solution, is lower than that of low density material, this may easily be an artifact of the test method. This statement is made in full knowledge of apparently contrary reports. Complete resolution of this riddle may be a long way off since even the classic "absolute" methods of molecular weight determination, such as osmotic pressure, are not completely free of anomalies due to incomplete solution, molecular weight distribution, etc. Evidently there is also little reason to assume a similar molecular weight for materials of like melt index. This discussion was brought up to explain the fact that high density polyethylene may not become available in high melt index or "easy flow" forms, and this may change the fields of application open to it.

A marked contrast to these properties, where density changes in the low ranges have relatively small effects compared to the changes in the higher ranges, is shown by the

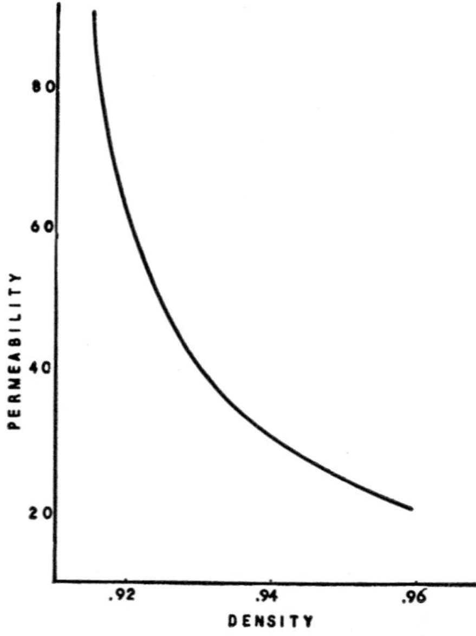

Figure 3–6. Change of carbon dioxide permeability with density.

carbon dioxide permeability (Figure 3-6). Here the density increment .92 to .93 has the largest influence and the change from .95 to .96 is insignificant. A similar, although not so striking relationship is found between density and vicat temperature (Figure 3-7) where the rate of increase decreases as the density goes up.

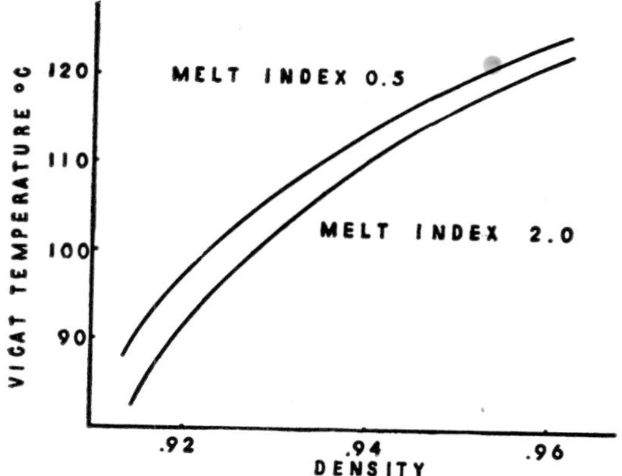

Figure 3–7. Change of vicat softening point with density.

The fact that these relations are not all linear and simple, frequently makes it possible to find a density range for a particular application where certain particularly important properties have been enhanced, with very little sacrifice of other desirable properties.

The problems involved in injection molding extremely high density polyethylene can be seen from Figure 3-8. This shows that the polyethylene melt has the same density, regardless of the density of the cold polymer, and that the high density material starts to set up at a higher temperature than the low density material. This means that in order to reach its final density when cold, the high density material has to shrink a great deal more. This is discussed in detail under injection molding.

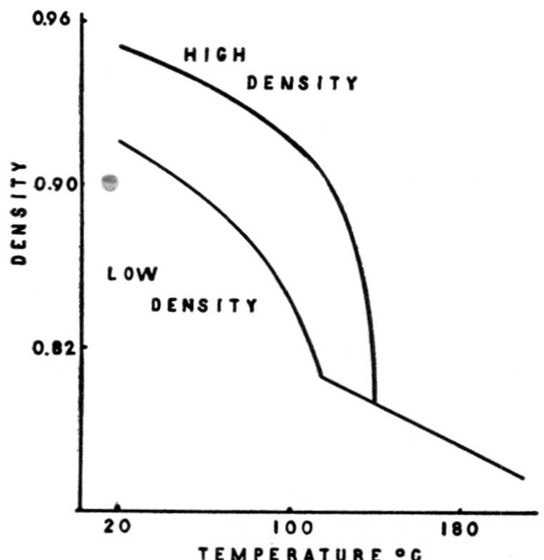

Figure 3–8. Change of density with temperature of two polyethylene samples with different room temperature densities.

Chemical Reactions of Polyethylene

The discussion so far has been related to chemistry only insofar as the physical tests discussed relate to molecular structure, but this is by no means the limit of polyethylene chemistry. Polyethylene does have chemical reactions, and they are significant technically as well as scientifically interesting.

They are, in general, the reactions that would be expected of an aliphatic hydrocarbon, taking into consideration the fact that it is extremely high in molecular weight.

Polyethylene undergoes oxidation, not only in the sense that it burns, but also in the sense that it absorbs oxygen at a rather rapid rate—above about 80°C. Initially, at least, this oxygen does not result in a breakdown of the chain, but rather in deterioration of its electrical properties, especially loss factor. It also results in increased melt viscosity, which in extrusion produces gels in the film. Eventually the absorption of oxygen will result in a material no longer thermoplastic. This stiffening is generally referred to as cross-linking, and infrared studies of oxidized polymers show the presence of keto groups that may link the chains together. As oxidation progresses, carboxylic acid groups also appear with decreasing molecular weight. It is possible to oxidize polyethylene to the point where it has an appreciable neutralization value, or acid number. This is only done commercially with low-molecular weight polyethylene and results in emulsifiable waxes useful in polishes and similar products.

Another useful technical application of oxidized polyethylene is its printability, which can be improved by treating its surface. Momentary exposure of the surface to high temperatures, whether by flame or radiant heat, produces polar, oxygen-containing groups on the surface, whose secondary forces make it possible for ordinary inks to adhere to the surface. The electrical discharge method produces a similar effect, partly as a result of the formation of ozone by the discharge which reacts with the surface. Chromic acid in strong acid solution has a similar effect, as do many other strongly oxidizing reagents.

However, for most purposes, oxidation is detrimental and in many cases antioxidants are added to inhibit it. One interesting fact related to this problem is that normal polyethylene in equilibrium with the atmosphere contains air in a quantity about 10 per cent of its volume. This means whenever polyethylene is heated to the point where it will react with oxygen, even out of contact with the atmosphere, oxygen will be available.

Polyethylene is readily chlorinated. As early as 1936 Fawcett and Myles produced a series of chlorinated polyethylenes by direct chlorination in solution. By changing the chlorine content a wide range of properties can be obtained, varying from those of normal polyethylene to approximately those of unplasticized polyvinyl chloride. Under present circumstances these are more expensive to make than polyvinyl chloride and appear to offer little advantage. It is also possible to chlorosulfonate polyethylene to produce an elastomer. This is a commercially available product with specialized appplications.

Although it is not a chemical reaction in the usual sense, the effect of x-radiation, or radiation from an atomic pile, deserves mention. Radiation produces free radicals in polyethylene which cross-link the molecules. A small amount of radiation causes no apparent changes in the material but increases its ability to retain its shape at high temperatures, while decreasing its susceptibility to stress cracking. Further radiation increases its hardness until it finally becomes weak and brittle. The effects of irradiation are similar to vulcanization in a rubber article. Commercial installations at present use x-ray equipment, but it appears likely that atomic energy developments will make available more economical sources of radiation. The use of Cobalt 60 has already reached commercial application. This and other methods of changing ethylene polymers will be discussed in Chapter 5.

4. MANUFACTURE OF POLYETHYLENE

The first requisite for the manufacture of polyethylene is a source of ethylene. In Britain this was obtained by the rather laborious and expensive method of hydrogenating acetylene obtained from the reaction of calcium carbide and water. In the United States ethylene is obtained as a by-product of petroleum refining. The various cracking operations yield a mixture of light hydrocarbons, saturated and unsaturated, which are separated by conventional petroleum refining procedures to give ethylene. Frequently a propane stream is cracked as an additional source.

Refinery ethylene is suitable for many chemical purposes but it is generally given a further purification for use in the manufacture of polyethylene. Figure 4-1 shows part of the refining section of a typical polyethylene plant.

The quality of the ethylene gas has to be carefully controlled if the polyethylene is to be uniform. Impurities in the gas fall into two general classes—inert impurities and active impurities. The inert impurities interfere with the reaction only mechanically by requiring a larger total pressure in the reactor in order to achieve a needed ethylene pressure. As reactor gas is recirculated in most polyethylene plants these impurities must be kept low, otherwise they build up. Some manufacturers have combined facilities where the ethylene, after one pass through the polyethylene reactor is used up in a less critical process, thus decreasing the harm caused by inert impurities.

Figure 4–1. Ethylene purification plant.
(*Courtesy Spencer Chemical Company*)

Active impurities are an entirely different matter. These are materials which enter into, or modify the course of the reaction directly. They can be divided into several classes.

Cross-linking agents—acetylene-butadiene
Copolymerizing monomers—carbon monoxide, propylene

Chain termination agents—hydrogen, methane, ethane, hydrogen sufide, carbon dioxide, nitrogen
Catalyst—oxygen, oxides of nitrogen

Such materials must be carefully controlled because even the smallest amounts will have a marked influence on the reaction and the nature of the resulting polymer. Once the purity of the ethylene has been assured it is necessary to raise it to the high pressures required for the reaction.

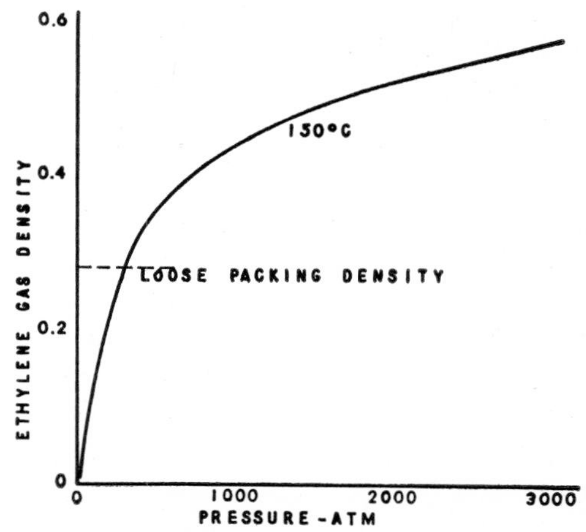

Figure 4–2. Change of ethylene gas density with pressure.

The pressure used in the commercial production of polyethylene is above 15,000 psi. It is difficult to imagine what such a pressure represents. In order to help understand it in terms of the gas molecule, Figure 4-2 shows the pressure of ethylene vs. density. It is evident that at 1000 atm. we are well beyond the point where the straight line relationship between pressure and density has broken down. The maximum density of loosely packed undistorted ethylene molecules is 0.28 g/cc calculated on a maximum molecular dimension of 5.5Å units. This density is obtained below 300 atm. at 150°C. Further compression causes much smaller density increases since the molecules are forced into each other and distorted by the pressure.

This extreme proximity of molecules evidently gives a particularly favorable environment for a growing polymer chain. The chances for the growing chain to encounter an ethylene molecule for further growth are very good indeed. While it is not true that there is a sharp stopping line below which polymer will not form, it is true that the higher the pressure the better the chances a growing chain has of reaching a long length.

The compression process presents formidable mechanical problems and a large power requirement. It represents the greatest cost in the production of polymer, so it follows that efficient operation of the compressors is absolutely essential to economical operation. One of the largest factors of this cost is the maintenance of equipment. Not only do these tremendous pressures exert fantastic forces on the equipment, particularly at the places where the gas must be sealed but evidently even the slightest defect in a seal causes a tremendous leakage. Leakage is serious not only because material is lost but also because it introduces grave hazards. A jet of gas escaping from even a pinhole at these pressures can cut flesh like a knife. A more subtle danger, however, which constantly threatens destruction of the entire operation is that ethylene gas is colorless, odorless and highly flammable, producing explosive mixtures with air over a rather wide range of compositions. As a result, all conceivable locations for leakage must be anticipated and any leaking gas led off where it will do no harm.

One technique for reducing the explosion hazard is to

enclose only those portions of the equipment that must be protected. Most of the piping, etc., is in the open where any leakage can be dissipated without building up dangerous concentrations. Recognition of the hazards involved has led to designs that make these operations models for safety and reliability. In addition to design for safety and economy, a well thought out and efficient maintenance program is essential. Most polyethylene plants have their own facilities for repairing equipment, repair parts are liberally stocked, and in addition to a regular maintenance schedule based on previous experience, all equipment is thoroughly and periodically checked for any sign of trouble before the scheduled shutdown. The plants are generally so arranged that any one component of a line can be cut out temporarily without shutting down the complete line.

Like all modern chemical plants, instrumentation is very complete, and all the significant operating variables are under automatic control.

In addition to automatic control of the plant, the product is sampled at short intervals and analyzed in the laboratory.

After the gas is compressed it is led through a reactor. These are commonly of two types—the autoclave and the tubular reactor. In the first, the compressed ethylene enters a chamber of considerable size in which the reaction occurs; in the second, it is reacted in a long tube.

A catalyst is introduced just before the reaction begins and more may be added at various intervals during the operation in order to control the reaction as desired. This catalyst initiates the reaction which is extremely rapid and exothermic. It is therefore essential to control the catalyst addition to prevent the reaction from getting out of hand. If the proportion of catalyst is too large, or if the feed gas contains traces of catalytic impurity, it is possible to get what is called a "decomp." When this happens the temperature rises rapidly, with an accompanying pressure rise that may destroy the reactor. Generally, there is no explosion but copious quantities of carbon are produced which are extremely difficult to clean out and which contaminate the product of the reactor for weeks afterward. Evidently this is not only dangerous but also expensive and has to be carefully guarded against.

In order to maintain control of the reaction, only a percentage of the ethylene is polymerized at each pass; the greatest part is merely recirculated to keep the temperature down. This requires separating the polymer from the unreacted gas.

Most of the gas is separated by permitting the product of the reactor to expand into a chamber substantially below reaction pressure. The expansion stops the reaction short at this point and thus is an important means of control. In expanding, the density of the gas is reduced and the polymer drops out. The gas is then recompressed and returned to the system. The polymer is now in a plastic state and is passed into another separator, or series of separators, at successively lower pressure, until all the gas has been removed. The last separation may be below atmospheric pressure. The polymer is taken out of the last separator by means of a screw extruder which may be equipped to homogenize and work the material.

The extruder forces the polymer through a die either in the form of strips or as small rods. The strip is usually run into a water bath where it is cooled, after which it is chopped into cubes. The rods may either be cut at the die face by a rapidly moving blade and dropped into water, giving a roughly spherical pellet, or they may be cooled and chopped, giving a pellet in the shape of a short prism or cylinder.

The cutter is generally the first place where a sample of the product can be obtained. Both continuous and spot check samples may be taken here for analysis. The product is now placed in a "hold" bin where it is kept until the sample check shows that it meets specifications, at which time it is transferred to storage bins.

Except for appearance and contamination, the most common control test is for melt viscosity, which is an indication of the average molecular weight of the polymer. The commonest measure of melt viscosity is the Melt Index developed by I.C.I., early in their development of polyethylene.

The Melt Indexer (Figure 4-3) is an extremely simple extrusion plastometer consisting of a thermostatically controlled cylinder supported in a vertical position. A piston rides in the cylinder, which has a small extrusion orifice at

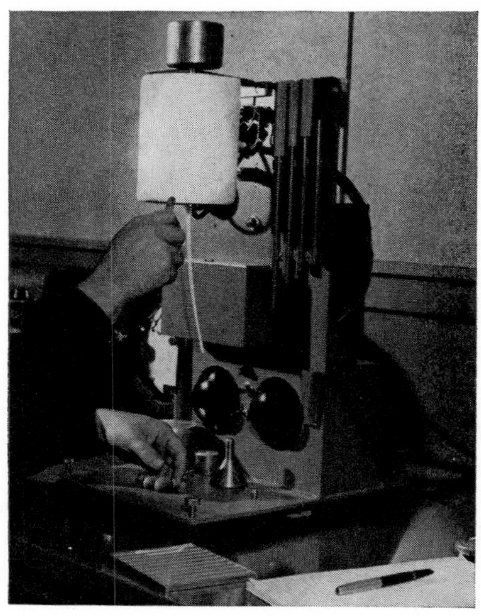

Figure 4–3. Melt Indexer in use.
(*Courtesy Spencer Chemical Company*)

the bottom of it. The piston is weighted by a standard weight. In order to get consistent and reproducible results, however, it is essential to maintain accurate temperature control and to adhere to dimensional tolerances.

In order to make a determination, the Melt Indexer is brought up to its standard temperature (190°C) and charged with 3 grams of the polymer under test on a closely prescribed time cycle. At the proper time the weighted piston is placed on the charge and extrusion commences through the orifice. The amount of material extruded in a given time is measured by cutting it off and weighing it on an analytical balance. The figure reported as melt index is the weight in grams extruded in 10 minutes. Another figure often determined on the Melt Indexer is called "per cent recovery of the Melt Indexer Strand" and is useful in predicting the processing characteristics of the polymer. It is determined by measuring the diameter of the strand extruded by the Melt Indexer at its widest point, subtracting the diameter of the orifice, and dividing the result by the orifice diameter. Times 100 this figure is called "per cent recovery"

ds=diameter of strand

do=diameter of Melt Indexer Orifice

$$\frac{ds-do}{do} \times 100 = \% \text{ recovery}$$

Although not commonly used, this figure is specified by some users of polyethylene. It is a measure of the rubbery or elastic property of polyethylene flow which is so important in understanding its processing characteristics. If the sample is very rubbery the strand will swell as it leaves the extrusion orifice because much of its flow was elastic, and when the pressure is relieved the elastic flow recovers its previous position, thus swelling the strand. In the absence of elastic components in the flow no such recovery occurs and the strand is no larger than the orifice. General experience with this value shows that a recovery of over 50 per cent indicates processing difficulties.

When a batch in hold bin is tested and found to comply with specifications it is sent to a storage hopper, and when this is full it is withdrawn to a blender. The blending is done to assure complete uniformity throughout a lot of material.

Several types of blenders are used, the most common ones being drum blenders and conical blenders in which the entire batch is tumbled over and over. Bucket blenders, like those used in the grain industry where streams of material are withdrawn from several places in a large bin and then returned to the top, are also used.

It is essential to protect the material from contamination during the blending operation. Extreme care must therefore be taken in designing the blender, not only to provide a tight method of closing, but also to make sure there are no wearing parts inside the blender which will introduce contamination. Maintenance and operation also have to be carefully performed to avoid accidental contamination. After blending, the sample is again tested, and if satisfactory the lot is placed in bags, drums, or bulk containers for shipment. Final check samples are taken from the packed product to assure compliance with specifications. The polyethylene leaving the reactor is not entirely satisfactory for many purposes and must be compounded with other ingredients, or in some cases "hot worked," to improve its processing characteristics. Hot working is analogous to "breaking" in the rubber industry and has a similar, although much less drastic effect on the properties of the material, that is to say, the rubbery or "nervy" character of the plastic mass is reduced. Contrary to the experience with rubber, little or no reduction in average molecular weight as evidenced by Melt Index occurs.

Figure 4–4. Banbury mixer.
(*Courtesy Farrel-Birmingham Corp.*)

The commonest compounding ingredient is carbon black. Since polyethylene is subject to degradation by sunlight, carbon black is added when it is used for permanent structures out of doors. It screens out the sunlight and limits any degradation to the surface layers. Polyethylene for pipe and electrical cable sheathing is commonly compounded with carbon black. The Banbury mixer (Figure 4-4) is generally used for this purpose. Other intensive mixers, two-roll mills, or compounding extruders can also be used.

In order to avoid unnecessary contamination some plants add a large percentage of the carbon black to some polyethylene in a remote location and then add this concentrate at the plant. This "master batch" operation not only eliminates dry carbon black from the plant but permits a more uniform dispersion of the black in the polyethylene.

For electrical purposes antioxidants are frequently incorporated in polyethylene. These protect the material from oxidative attacks during high temperature processing, permit easier rework of the scrap, and improve the service life of the product. Many well-known rubber antioxidants are satisfactory for use with polyethylene and some have been developed particularly for it. While some of the best antioxidants are toxic it is now possible to obtain others which are completely nonpoisonous.

Polyethylene is colored by compounding it with a wide variety of dyes and pigments. This subject deserves a complete book because of the variety of problems presented. Many of the colors used in the plastic industry are entirely unsatisfactory for polyethylene. The entire class of oil-soluble dyes has to be eliminated due to migration and blooming of the color. The polyethylene piece which rubbed color off on everything it touched was all too common in the early days of the industry.

Inorganic pigments, in general, are more satisfactory, but even here care must be taken because certain metals, manganese in particular, cause decomposition and bad odors. Some easily reduced pigments such as chrome yellow may fade at high processing temperatures, and hydrated oxides must be avoided. Considerable use is also made of dyes converted to lakes. These are considerably troublesome in dispersion but certain colors are available in no other way. By no means all manufacturers of polyethylene do color work. Many prefer to make only natural resin and have colored material made up by custom compounders.

Another general class of polyethylene compounding materials comprises lubricants or "slip agents," consisting of materials of a fatty or waxy nature. These help processing by increasing flow, facilitating mold release in injection molding, or assisting roll release in calendering. They also alter the properties of the finished product. The largest use of "slip agents" is in the manufacture of polyethylene film. They reduce the frictional coefficient of the polyethylene film thus facilitating its passage over the automatic equipment used in the packaging industry. The use of these materials has been tremendous during the last few years and film with almost any desired frictional coefficient can now be produced.

Another class of compounding ingredients, elastomers, has been used since the earliest commercial production of polyethylene. Polyisobutylene is the classic example, although any elastomer, vulcanizable or not, can be used. The main purpose of elastomer addition is to reduce the tendency of the polyethylene to crack under stress, in the presence of sensitizing agents. Elastomers also have some value as processing aids and are sometimes added to calendering compositions to increase the hot strength of the sheet. Depending on the amount used, the elastomers affect the properties of the article produced; the elastomer compounds are usually softer and more rubbery.

After being compounded the polyethylene is pelleted in much the same manner as the plain polymer; it is bagged and shipped in the same way.

The discussion here has been limited to the traditional high-pressure polymerization of ethylene, but increasing quantities of polyethylene are now being made by a variety of "low pressure" methods.

In their efforts to control polymer properties, investigators borrowed from previous knowledge of ethylenic polymerization. This indicated that simple mass polymerization with peroxide catalysts was capable of only limited flexibility, and that solution, emulsion, or suspension polymers could be made having a wider variety of properties.

The gaseous nature of the monomer made the possibility of solution polymerization, where the monomer could be brought into the reaction system by solution in a solvent at moderate pressures, very attractive. The first problems encountered using this system were to find suitable catalysts for producing a useful polymer. Ziegler patented a method for making a catalyst composed of titanium tetrachloride and an aluminum alkyl which successfully produced a high polymer from ethylene, closely resembling the polymethylenes of Buckley, Cross and Ray. This catalyst system has been put into commercial production but presents some serious problems, one being that the aluminum alkyl (usually aluminum triethyl or aluminum tri-isobutyl) is difficult to produce and difficult to use; among other things, it becomes pyrophoric if exposed to air and it decomposes rapidly in the presence of moisture.

A more stable catalyst system has been developed by Standard Oil Company (Indiana) using a nickel oxide catalyst supported on charcoal or a molybdena-alumina catalyst. Before it is used in polymerization the catalyst must be activated by reduction with hydrogen. Like the Ziegler system, the catalyst is insoluble in the solvent used to carry the ethylene, producing a heterogeneous system which has certain marked advantages.

The ethylene is dissolved in an organic solvent such as xylene and pressured up to about 1000 psi before coming in contact with the catalyst. The polymerization pressure is not critical but the temperature should be as low as possible, in the neighborhood of 400°F, to give the highest yield of solid polymer. The polymer is precipitated from the solvent after removal of the catalyst and any remaining solvent is evaporated off, giving a product essentially free from catalyst.

Resins made in this manner resemble the polymethylene

mentioned previously, being stronger, harder, and less permeable than normal polyethylene. They have a higher specific gravity and a higher degree of crystallinity. They also show less chain branching than normal polyethylene. It appears from the nature of the process that greater control of the properties of the polymer is possible than with the high-pressure process. This process is also useful for the production of polymers from other l-olefins and copolymers of ethlene with other l-olefins having a wide range of physical properties.

These catalysts are by no means the only ones capable of effecting polymerization of ethylene at low pressures. There has been a rapid development of new catalyst systems for this purpose and at present seventeen workable low-pressure catalyst systems have been reported. While low-pressure polymerization produces high density polyethylene having the general properties expected of that material, low-pressure polymers are by no means identical with one another. Different catalysts produce materials differing significantly in properties.

5. PROCESSING OF POLYETHYLENE

Polyethylene is made into useful products by a number of different processes. From a point of view of material consumed, the most important method of processing polyethylene is by extrusion. While the term "extrusion" can properly be used to describe any process which forces a material through a die in order to shape it, it has acquired a much more limited meaning as related to polyethylene processing.

Extrusion

The polyethylene extruder usually consists of a metal cylinder containing a closely fitting rotable helical screw. It operates on the same principle as the ordinary meat grinder, the only difference being that in order to make a coherent product after passing through the machine, the polyethylene must be melted. This requires heating the cylinder long enough to provide thorough heating and mixing of the material.

Figure 5-1 shows three screw designs used in machines for extruding polyethylene. Numbers 1 and 2 are the most satisfactory. In addition to helical flights for conveying the material forward, these are provided with a mixing or metering head which assures thorough melting and homogenizing of the material.

The cylinder is generally heated by electrical resistance

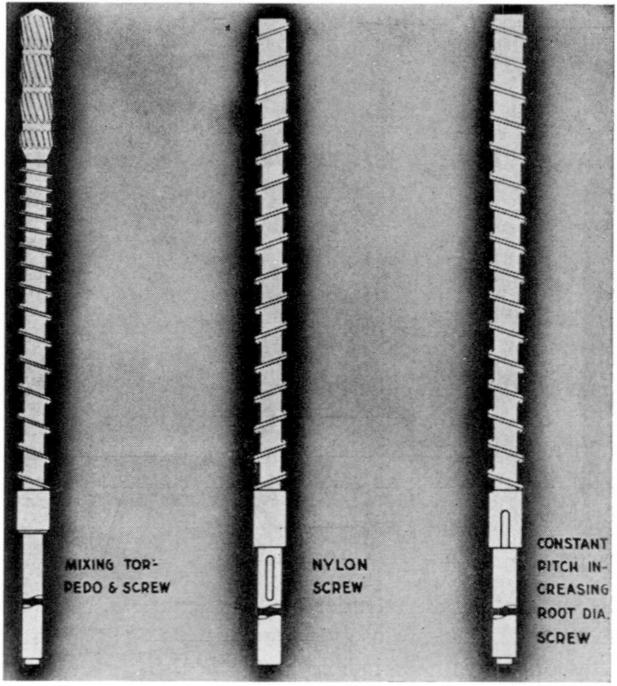

Figure 5–1. Three types of extrusion screws used for polyethylene extrusion. (*Courtesy Dow Chemical Company*)

heaters, although hot oil is entirely practicable and sometimes even preferred. The temperature is regulated by means of thermocouples set into the cylinder wall; these control the heat input to the heaters by means of an automatic controller. The controllers vary from simple on-off designs to very complex mechanisms for balancing heat output against needs. The most common is the proportioning-type controller which starts to reduce the heat input as the control point is reached, and which continues to heat a little even at the control point. In addition to the type of controller used, the location of the thermocouples is important for good control. Figure 5-2 shows a typical modern extruder.

Figure 5–2. A typical modern extruder.
(*Courtesy National Rubber Machinery Corp.*)

In Europe, a wide variety of multiple-screw machines is also used in addition to the type mentioned above. In these the single screw is replaced by two or more intermeshing screws, which by their interaction exert a more positive forward push on the material. Unfortunately, the same action which assures a positive forward push generally decreases the heating and mixing action so essential to good extrusion. This means that the plastic frequently reaches the die unevenly heated, resulting in rough or wavy extrusions. Another peculiarity of these machines is that their action of trapping a portion of plastic and conveying it forward practically by positive displacement, also results in trapping and extruding air, which produces holes in the product. Accurate control of the bulk factor of the feed and of the amount of feed is essential to satisfactory operation. These machines appear to be quite sensitive to the physical shape of the polymer fed.

Polyethylene film for packaging is commonly produced by extrusion. There are two general methods of extruding polyethylene film—blown tubing and flat film. In blown tubing the polyethylene is extruded through a circular die orifice in the form of a tube, which is carried some distance from the die and then pinched together. Air is then introduced into the tube between the die and the pinch rolls to balloon it out, or it can be expanded over a metal guide. The tube may be inflated only slightly above die size, or may be three or four times as large, thus permitting a variety of sizes to be produced on one die. The air determines the diameter of the bubble, and thus the size of the tube. Alternatively, a confining tube may regulate the size. The thickness of the wall is regulated by balancing the draw off speed at the pinch rolls against the output of the extruder. Blown tubing may be extruded either horizontally or vertically. The commonest practice in the United States is to run the bubble up. Figure 5-3 shows a typical blown-tubing installation. Figure 5-4 shows a typical die used for this process.

The length of the bubble between the die and pinch roll is important because the tube will stick together if pinched when it is too hot. Air is blown against the surface of the tube to cool it; control of this air is very important.

Maintaining an even thickness around the periphery of the bubble is one of the major problems in manufacturing blown film. In the first place, the die must be so designed as to supply an even flow of resin all around. In many of the

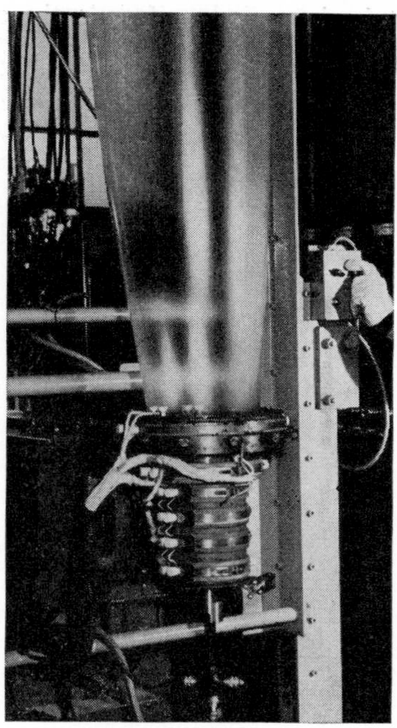

Figure 5–3. Polyethylene blown film extrusion.
(*Courtesy Modern Plastics Machinery Co.*)

designs the plastic coming into the die splits flow around the center mandrel of the die and joins again on the other side after which it traverses a considerable distance in fairly narrow channels to the die lips. An alternative design holds the center mandrel on a web or "spider" and the flow passes through the spider into the passage around the mandrel.

This design substitutes a large number of small weld lines for the one large one found in the previous die. The final thickness depends on the exact control of the air supplied for cooling. If the tube is cooled uniformly the slight variation in flow at the die will stretch out even.

Figure 5–4. Vertical die typical of those used for production of polyethylene blown film.
(*Courtesy National Rubber Machinery Corp.*)

The properties of blown film are largely dependent on the method of extrusion as well as on the resin used. The operator can vary an operation to produce tubing to meet a customer's requirements.

The output in most plants is largely limited by their ability to cool the extruded tube to the point where it will not stick together when pinched. This is called "blocking," and means that, other things being equal, the operator prefers to extrude as cool as possible. Blown film is usually extruded at 300 to 350°F, at which temperature the melt is distinctly more rubbery than viscous. Considering the bubble-blowing nature of the process this is evidently an advantage, since a truly viscous melt would not maintain cohesion for this operation. This means, however, that when the melt is suddenly chilled very appreciable strains are frozen in, and the resulting film shows distinct orientation and has different physical properties in the two directions. The ratio of the drawing, and resulting strains in the two directions, evidently depend on how much the bubble was blown up above die size. At exactly die size, all drawing is in the direction of the tube movement; the blow ratio determines the drawing in the other direction. Properly controlled orientation improves the strength of polyethylene film, particularly its resistance to impact. Film produced by blowing a bubble two or more times the diameter of the die will be stronger than film produced under otherwise identical conditions, but with less of a blow ratio. It is common practice to extrude blown film at lower blow ratios than this because the use of a very small die reduces the amount of material that can be put through it, and thus increases the cost of the film. For most applications this is unimportant since polyethylene film has more strength than necessary anyway.

Polyethylene film is also produced by the flat-die process. As the name implies, the polyethylene is extruded out of a narrow slit in a long, straight die, which may be end-fed or center fed. The latter, also called a "Tee die," is more commonly used for wide sheeting. Figure 5-5 shows a complete flat die unit.

In contrast to blown film, which is generally used for small tubing to be made directly into bags by cutting a length and sealing one end, flat film is usually made in considerable widths, on large machines at high production rates. Since the stretching of the film is necessarily in one direction only, this process cannot take advantage of the strengthening properties of biaxial orientation. In fact, orientation in one direction only has a tendency to weaken the film in the other direction.

Figure 5–5. Unit for the production of polyethylene film by flat die method. (*Courtesy of Modern Plastics Machinery Corp.*)

In this process, the orientation must be minimized in order to get the best properties. This is done by using much higher temperatures which decrease the elastic properties of the melt and permit a high rate of draw in one direction without setting up excessive strains. The higher temperatures also produce a clearer film. Flat film may be extruded around 500°F.

Flat die film is usually extruded downward into a water bath which cools and sets the film. The temperature of the bath and its distance from the die lip have a great effect on the properties of the film. Alternatively, it may be extruded either horizontally or downward and cooled by contact with a water-cooled chill roll, thus preventing the water spotting usually associated with a water bath. The equipment used for flat film may also be used for sheeting up to about .060 inch thick. The horizontal dies extruding to a chill roll are particularly well adapted for the heavier gauges and may be used up to .125 inch thick if the opening of the die is wide enough.

The chill roll is generally followed by two other highly polished rolls, the three working as a calender stack to polish the surface of the sheet. This is the same type of equipment used for impact styrene sheet, and it is often used for both purposes.

Extrusion Coating. Equipment similar to that for making flat film is used for the extrusion coating of paper, cloth and other continuous webs. In this process a downward extruding slit die is used which differs from the flat film die only to the extent that the die body generally slants back sharply from the die lips thus permitting the lips to come closer to the nip of the two rolls which are just below the die. One is a large water-cooled chill roll which may be polished or matté finished, depending on the surface desired on the coating. The other, a rubber-covered pressure roll, runs against the chill roll. It is held against the chill roll by hydraulic or air cylinders and can be withdrawn for starting up. The die is located directly above the point of contact of the two rollers, with the die lips about three inches above the point of contact.

In order to coat a continuous web, the web is run over the pressure roll and through the nip of the two rolls. Polyethylene is extruded through the die and onto the web. The rolls force the web and coating into close contact, promoting adhesion. The coated web follows the chill roll until it is properly cooled and it is then stripped off.

If it is desirable to place a layer of polyethylene between two webs, or merely to apply polyethylene as an adhesive between two webs, the same machine can be used but a second web is led over the chill roll, and the polyethylene is extruded between the two webs. A continuous line seal can be made by extruding a thin ribbon of polyethylene between two sheets of polyethylene, or any other material.

In addition to coatings of pure polyethylene a large amount of extrusion coating is done with polyethylene-wax mixtures. The wax blend cannot generally be coated much thinner than pure polyethylene, but the surface of the coating is less tacky, so the laminate is easier to use, higher coating speeds are possible in some cases, and, of course, the wax is cheaper.

Pipe Extrusion. After film and sheeting, the most important use of the extrusion process is for the manufacture of polyethylene pipe. The apparatus is identical, up to the die, which resembles that used for thin tubing except that instead of being turned up it is used horizontally. It is also commonly attached to an elbow at the extruder so that the line of the pipe is parallel to the body of the extruder. This is known as an "offset" die and is shown in Figure 5-6.

Figure 5–6. Offset type die for production of polyethylene pipe. (*Courtesy National Rubber Machinery Corp.*)

The die orifice is, of course, quite different from that of a film die, being smaller in diameter and having a wider opening. The uniformity of wall thickness is controlled by adjusting screws which move the collar or bushing which forms the exterior of the pipe; the center core remains stationary. Once the polyethylene pipe has emerged from the die it must be supported in shape and cooled. It may also be given a final sizing after it leaves the die.

Three systems are commonly used for supporting and cooling polyethylene pipe, the most common of which is known as the internal mandrel. In this system a tapered mandrel ending in about the finished inside diameter of the pipe is rigidly supported from the front of the extrusion die core. The mandrel may be anywhere from 6 to 18 inches long. It may be chrome-plated and polished but a fine matté or "vapor hone" finish is preferred. It may even be knurled. The pipe emerges from the die and passes over the mandrel, being drawn against it by the decrease in diameter resulting from the pull of the haul-off mechanism.

It is extremely important to control the temperature of the cold water which is circulated through the mandrel to cool it. While the pipe is passing over the mandrel and being cooled, water is being poured over the outside, chilling that as well. Pipe made in this way generally shows "water markings" on the outside. These can be substantially prevented by various expedients which assure a steady line contact between the water and the hot pipe.

Another common method for supporting the pipe during cooling is called the external sizing ring. In this method air pressure is maintained inside the pipe to prevent its collapse, either by plugging the end of the pipe or by means of a floating plug or "bird," attached to the die core by means of a wire. The die must be arranged to permit air to enter the pipe through the core. An adequate supply of air at an accurately controlled pressure must be available. After leaving the die the pipe passes through a series of rings of decreasing size, the last of which is at the finished outside diameter of the pipe. These rings hold the pipe round and size it accurately. The pipe is generally kept under cold water after the first sizing ring which forms the entrance of a water tank, but sometimes there are several rings in the air which are cooled only by air jets.

A third method employs a sizing tube or chamber. This resembles the above method except that the rings are replaced by a cooled tube. Many modifications of this method have been developed by individual plants, including a means of introducing controlled air pressure between the pipe and the cooling tube and the introduction of fluids other than air to prevent sticking.

A variation of the external sizing chamber method—the vacuum-sizing die—is common in Europe, but less well known in the United States. The cooling tube used in this system consists of three sections, the first and third of which are cooled by circulating water. The center section is perforated with fine holes which communicate to a chamber, maintained slightly below atmospheric pressure by means of a pump. Since this vacuum holds the pipe against the die, no internal pressure in the tube is necessary. This eliminates the need to plug the end of the pipe, and thus there is no danger of diameter fluctuations when the finished pipe has to be cut. Accurate control of the suction, which is essential, occasionally presents a problem at the startup. The vacuum die generally acts as the entrance to a water bath and any leakage results in water in the vacuum line. Usually the water bath is divided to permit emptying the part immediately against the vacuum die during startup.

This sizing system is quite highly developed and it is

possible to buy a chamber with water and vacuum connections so arranged that a variety of inserts can be used for different pipe sizes. This facilitates changing sizes and eliminates duplicating the entire construction for each size.

The interior of the sizing die has a matté finish to prevent sticking. These dies are operated at varying distances from the extrusion die, a longer air gap giving more operating difficulty but improving the surface finish on the pipe.

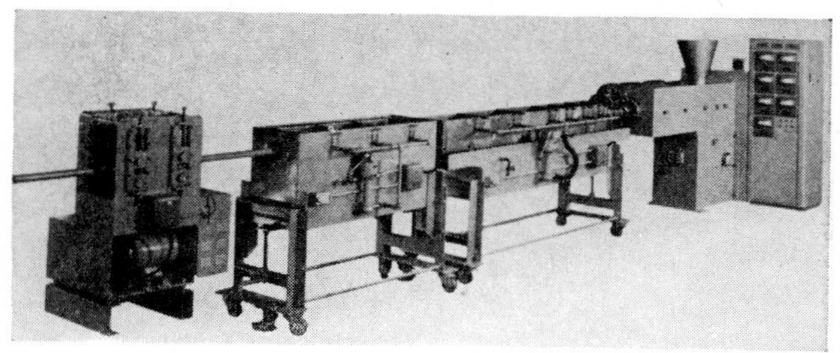

Figure 5–7. Unit for extrusion of polyethylene pipe. (*Courtesy Modern Plastic Machinery Corp.*)

Regardless of the initial method of cooling, once the pipe has been cooled sufficiently to hold its shape it is immersed in a tank of cold water where it is further cooled. After this it enters a haul-off unit which pulls it at a controlled rate, and it is imprinted with a brand name and reeled up. Figure 5-7 shows a pipe extrusion operation. Small size pipe and tubing can be made without using a mandrel or sizing die.

Pipe extrusion is ordinarily carried out at relatively low temperatures, 300-350°F stock temperature being average, and the die may be kept at a lower temperature to assist in setting up the pipe.

Wire Insulation. Extrusion is also used for wire insulation —one of the first and still most important uses for polyethylene. The equipment resembles that used for pipe, the main difference being that the die is generally not "offset" but extrudes out at right angles to the extruder barrel, in a horizontal plane (see Figure 5-8). The core of the die is modified to permit a wire to pass through it into the plastic mass before it emerges from the die.

Figure 5–8. Crosshead type die for insulation of wire. (*Courtesy National Rubber Machinery Corp.*)

The plastic is then shaped against the wire by the die orifice. Accurate control of the wire travel and extrusion rate is essential to the production of good wire. Adhesion between the wire and plastic is controlled by wire and compound temperature. After leaving the die the plastic may be "flame polished" to improve its appearance. In some cases, this also improves the insulating qualities of the coating. The wire is then cooled in a water trough, and checked by a spark tester in the line to detect any pin holes or other defects in the insulation. It then goes to the capstan which maintains constant speed on the wire, and it is then reeled up.

Miscellaneous Extrusions. Various strips and profiles such as ornamental belting, gaskets, welting, and the like are also made by extrusion. These are made very similarly except for the shape of the die used.

Many special polyethylene compounds have been developed for extrusion purposes which differ appreciably from those used for molding, and in many cases they greatly affect the final properties of the product.

Special resins that give particularly clear film, or that produce film having special frictional properties are used for film extrusion. Wire and cable-coating compounds with closely controlled electrical properties are available. Cable-sheathing compounds of particularly tough resin, incorporating carbon black and antioxidants for protection against the effects of light and oxygen are also made.

Wire coating is one field in which the use of radiation to improve the properties of the product has made rapid strides. Since the relatively poor heat resistance of polyethylene insulation is one of its chief drawbacks, irradiation is particularly valuable in this application. Also, the small and regular cross sections of the insulation on wire make it relatively easy to build equipment to irradiate it. Irradiation is also important in making tapes for electrical insulation, where evidently the same considerations apply.

Injection Molding

The other large-volume method of processing polyethylene is injection molding. In this process polyethylene is put into a heated cylinder and pushed through it by means of a ram, which is usually hydraulically operated. As the material passes through the cylinder it encounters a spreader or some other mechanism for bringing it in contact with the heated metal surfaces which melt it. The commonest form of spreader is a torpedo suspended in the cylinder leaving a narrow annular passage between it and the cylinder wall. Multiple tubular openings in a solid block are also commonly used. Figure 5-9 shows a modern injection molding machine.

Figure 5–9. Modern injection molding machine.
(*Courtesy Improved Machinery Co.*)

The most recent development in injection molding heater cylinders is the internal fin heater, also called a melt extraction heating chamber. This consists of a structure with fins that extend into the plastic to heat it and a large number of small holes to permit passage of the molten material and to prevent passage of unmelted particles.

The melted material passes through a nozzle into a closed die of the same size and shape as the desired article. The ram, mentioned previously, forces the plastic into the die. Evidently a great deal of the work done by the plunger is expended moving material through the heater. The design of the heater must minimize these frictional losses if the machine is to have adequate filling capacity. The ideal compromise between frictional losses and heating efficiency is not the same for polyethylene as for most other plastics. When polyethylene is molded at maximum output on a machine with a conventional heater there is a tendency for unmelted cubes to force their way through the center of the heater passage without melting. These appear as hard spots in the finished molding.

Narrowing the passages of the conventional heater will prevent this phenomenon which is commonly called "by-passing." However, the narrow passages have increased frictional resistance and decreased machine capacity. The internal fin heaters developed to combat this problem have shown good results in some cases.

An expedient used on the old type machine to eliminate by-passing, and at the same time to improve the distribution of dry color within the molding, is to insert a color dispersing unit into the machine nozzle. This consists of a small double strainer which breaks up the cold particles.

Like the narrow heater passages, this unit increases back pressure and decreases machine capacity. There also has been some feeling that, by raising the level of injection pressure required, the machine maintenance costs are increased.

For many years polyethylene injection moldings commonly suffered from a defect, known as "delamination;" which caused the finished piece to peel off in thin layers around the point where the material entered the die. This is caused by the rubbery nature of the melted polyethylene. In recent years the introduction of special molding resins which melt to a more fluid state, changes in mold design, and improved methods of heating the resin have reduced this problem.

Polyethylene, particularly the high-flow resins mentioned above, is probably the best thermoplastic for extremely large moldings, some of which will be discussed in the following chapters. The only size limitation apparently is to get a machine large enough to melt the charge and handle the mold. There is no indication that we have as yet approached a limit.

Polyethylene has also shown remarkable adaptability at the other end of the scale. It is widely used for small caps and closures which are generally made on some sort of an automatic machine. Many of the best completely automatic injection molding operations run on polyethylene. The properties that make it particularly adaptable to automatic operation are the softness of the finished piece which prevents mold damage when a piece is accidently caught in the mold, freedom from sticking, and the uniformity of the operating characteristics of the material. Properly molded polyethylene will reproduce mold detail with a great deal of accuracy and a good operating automatic molding machine will produce parts of great uniformity in size and physical properties.

Considerable light has been shed on the problems of injection molding polyethylene by the use of a glass-walled mold. This has shown that normal low-melt index polyethylene does not flow into the mold like other familiar thermoplastics. Polystyrene or acetate will form a "ball" at the gate and the plastic will flow into the mold in a smoothly curved "front." In low-melt index polyethylene the smooth curve of the front will crack and break up giving a crumbly effect not unlike a head of cauliflower. The mechanics of this formation is that the elastic component of the flow is extremely high so that stresses exceed the tensile strength of the melt, causing it to fracture. These successive fractures produce the rough surface common to polyethylene moldings until recently. Higher melt index polyethylene obviates this effect. Higher injection temperatures and slow speed injection may also help.

Miscellaneous Methods

In addition to the above processes, polyethylene can also be made into useful articles by several other methods. Many of these are secondary processes which depend on the preliminary production of an intermediate product by one of the preceding methods, the final product being made by a later process. The principal one of these is bottle blowing.

Bottle Blowing. In the blow-molding process a "parison" is first produced either by extrusion or by injection molding. This consists of a simple closed tube which, while still hot, is inserted into a hollow mold having the shape of the desired bottle. Air under pressure is then introduced inside the tube and it is blown out to the shape of the mold. In addition to conventional bottles, hollow shapes of many kinds can be made by this process. At present, sizes up to about 15-gallon carboys are made.

Sheet Forming. Another versatile method of producing a wide variety of shapes from polyethylene is sheet forming. A number of techniques are employed all of which use a polyethylene sheet, generally extruded. The sheet is heated and brought into contact with a forming die or jig which shapes it to the desired dimensions. In some cases a hot sheet, direct from the extruder, is used to eliminate the heating.

Vacuum Forming. The methods most commonly used are vacuum and vacuum-drape forming. The same machine, one of which is shown in Figure 5-10 is generally used for both of these methods.

Figure 5–10. Removal of formed pieces from vacuum-forming machine. (*Courtesy Spencer Chemical Co.*)

Although vacuum-forming machines operate in several ways, in the oldest and simplest one the cycle of operation is as follows:

(1) The plastic sheet is clamped tightly across the top of an air-tight box, which contains the mold, or is the mold.

(2) An electric radiant heater is moved into position over the plastic sheet and left there until the sheet is softened to a rubbery consistency.

(3) The heater is removed and a vacuum is drawn in the box or mold. This pulls the sheet down into the mold so that it takes the shape of the mold.

(4) After the piece has cooled enough to harden again the clamp is opened, and the sheet is removed from the mold.

(5) At this point the part is formed but it is still attached to the part of the sheet that was in the clamp. It must now be taken to a cutting press which trims the edge, giving a finished piece.

Vacuum-forming machines are presently available with automatic cut-off mechanisms (Figure 5-11) which eliminate the need for a separate trimming operation. The same mech-

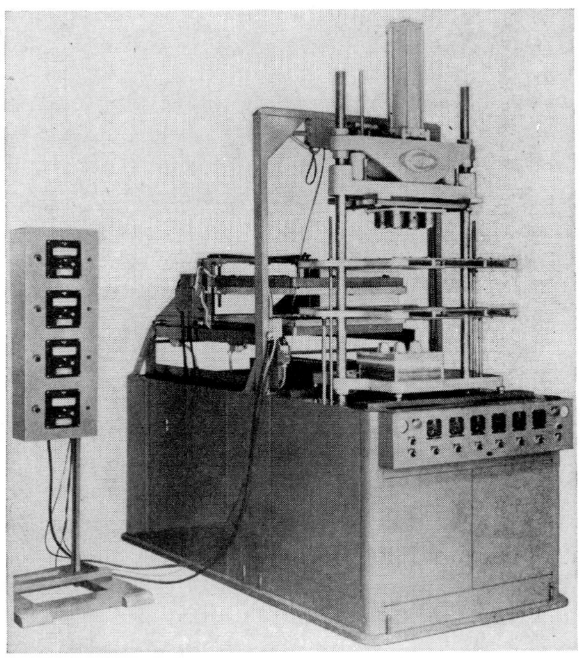

Figure 5–11. Vacuum-forming machine with provision for automatic trimming. (*Courtesy Vacuum Forming Corp.*)

anism that operates the cut-off also provides for a plug assist which permits the production of straight-sided pieces, or very deep draws without excessive thinning at the bottom. These machines can vacuum-form parts like flat bottom vials or collapsible tubes, and thus increase the scope of the vacuum-forming technique.

The cycle of operations for this type of machine is as follows:

(1) The sheet is clamped in a movable frame held well above the mold.

(2) Two heaters are used, one above and one below the sheet to reduce the time required to heat it to the necessary rubbery consistency.

(3) The heaters are removed and a plug or "assist" is brought down to the sheet. At the same time the clamp is moved down so it comes into contact with the mold.

(4) A vacuum is then drawn in the mold, pulling the plastic down into the shape of the mold.

(5) The plug comes down into the mold with the sheet and thus helps to mold the product. A cut-off knife on the plug cuts the unit away from the sheet.

(6) After the sheet is cooled the plug and clamp are moved up and the part is blown out of the mold by air pressure. In this way the molded part and trim are removed separately, eliminating the extra trimming operation.

It may be necessary when forming heavy sheet to use more force than is available from a vacuum in order to shape the sheet. In this case, the space above the sheet is sealed to the edge of the sheet, and the sheet is forced against the mold by pressure from above, sometimes in combination with vacuum on the die side.

In plug and ring forming a heated sheet is forced over a male mold by means of a ring which fits over the male, leaving just enough clearance for the plastic. When vacuum is also applied to the male mold this becomes drape-vacuum forming with a mechanical assist.

The most exact method of sheet forming is the matched die method, in which both a male and a female die are used, carefully matched so that when they are closed in a press there is just enough space for the plastic. This is essentially a form of compression molding. It permits close reproduction of detail on both faces of the plastic sheet, while the other methods can only imprint detail on the side in contact with the mold.

The simplest method of sheet forming is simple bending. This is limited to shapes having curves on only one plane, and cannot be used for compound curves. It is commonly used in conjunction with hot-gas welding to produce a variety of forms, such as tanks, ducts, etc.

Hot-Gas Welding. Hot-gas welding of polyethylene resembles the welding of metal in many ways. The sheets to be used for an assembly are first cut and bent into the proper shape so that they will fit together closely. One or both sides of the joint is chamfered out to give a vee-groove for the welding material, which consists of a thin rod, either of pure polyethylene, or of polyethylene compounded to improve its heat stability and adhesion.

The welding "torch" is a device that supplies a stream of inert gas, usually nitrogen or carbon dioxide, at about 700° F. The heating may be accomplished either by electric resistance heaters or by a gas flame. In the latter case, it should be noted that the flame never contacts the plastic but merely heats the stream of inert gas. A welding gun is shown in Figure 5-12.

In hot-gas welding a piece of welding rod is pressed into the groove of the joint and a stream of hot gas is placed on the rod and on the edges of the groove in order to melt the

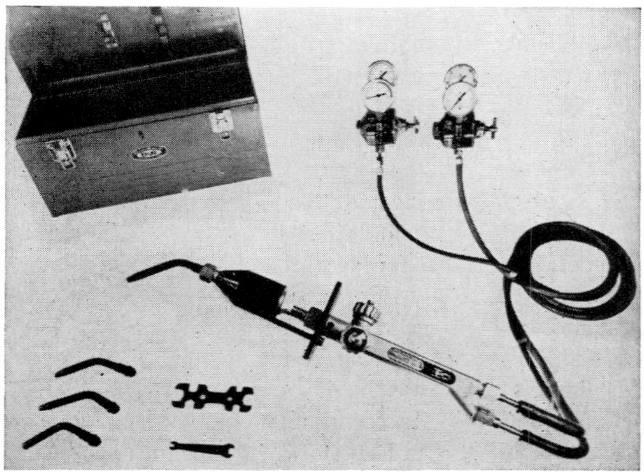

Figure 5–12. Welding torch suitable for use with polyethylene. (*Courtesy D&R Plastic Welders, Inc.*)

surfaces of both the rod and the groove. As the rod softens it is gradually pressed into the groove so that the melted rod and groove surface will fuse together. In the case of thick sheets several rods may be laid in successively to complete the joint. This technique is particularly useful for fabricating large pieces or for pieces of moderate size for one-of-a-kind or very small production.

In general, sheet-forming methods show a lower tooling up cost than injection molding but higher material and labor costs. They may compete with some injection moldings but in general they are best adapted to short runs and products that need to be changed frequently and rapidly.

Calendering. Although the greatest part of polyethylene sheeting is made by extrusion, it can be produced in several other ways, the most important of which is calendering. In this process a hot plastic mass of polyethylene is fed into the nip of the first pair of a series of steel rollers. In order to pass through the nip, it is formed into a sheet. The series of rolls is so arranged that the sheet passes through a series of roll nips, usually three in all, which form it more accurately and smoothly. It then passes part way around the last roll and is stripped off by a pull-off roll. This process has several advantages over extrusion, principally in the production of colored sheet. From its nature, the calender can go from one color to another without contamination or mixing while the extruder has to be cleaned out between colors. It is also practicable to calender sheet more highly loaded with fillers, than can be conveniently done by extrusion. Calendered sheet tends to have a duller surface than extruded sheet, and for some applications, such as fabric replacement, this is preferred. Calendered sheet is frequently used for vacuum forming. The calendering process may also be used as a means of coating a web. A modern plastic film calender is shown in Figure 5-13.

Figure 5–13. Modern plastic sheet calender suitable for polyethylene sheet production. (*Courtesy Farrel-Birmingham, Inc.*)

Extremely heavy sheet cannot be conveniently produced either by extrusion or by calendering. It may be made in one of two ways—press lamination or compression molding.

In press lamination, calendered or extruded sheets are laid upon one another to the desired thickness. The layers are then placed between polished plates and put in a press with cored platens, and heated until the sheets fuse together. The press is then cooled until the combined sheet can be handled. For very heavy laminations the edges of the sheet must be confined by a frame.

A special type of press lamination is the "skived block" method. This is the oldest method of plastic sheet production, dating back to the celluloid days. It had some use in the early days of polyethylene but is seldom used now. It has the advantage of producing a sheet that shows the maximum density and degree of crystallinity possible with the particular resin. In this method rough sheets or slabs of polyethylene are laid up in a heavy rectangular steel box, which is placed in a press where a closely fitting rectangular piston rides on the stack of slabs. The mass is slowly heated until it fuses under the pressure of the piston, and it is then slowly cooled. Since the blocks may be up to 9 inches thick, the heating and cooling is a very slow process, permitting maximum crystallization. The cooled block is then cut into sheets of the desired thickness by a sheeter. This is a heavy planer which simply drives a sharp knife through the block.

In compression molding, polyethylene granules are placed into a steel mold the size of the desired sheet.

Roller Coating. Polyethylene-wax blends can also be coated to various substrates by roller coating methods similar to those used for wax. Roller coating is used mostly for mixtures having lower percentages of polyethylene and has the advantage of higher speeds. Speeds up to 600 fpm are possible against a maximum of about 400 fpm for extrusion coating. Adhesion of the film to the web is also better with roller coating than by extrusion, especially at coating weights below 10# per ream which is a thickness of about .00075 inch.

Powder Techniques. Polyethylene can be coated on metal, and to a limited extent, it can be made into shapes by two techniques which use powdered polyethylene. The powder may be produced from granular polyethylene by mechanical grinding, using either a Banbury mixer or a two-roll mill at a suitable temperature, or the product of low-pressure polymerization may be isolated in the form of a fine powder and used. In the first method, known as "flame spraying," the polyethylene powder is blown through a gas flame which melts it and impinged on a metal surface where the melted particles coalesce into a continuous coating. If the metal is clean, and hot enough, the coating will stick. If the metal is greasy or cool the coating can be removed fairly easily and thus serves as a method of forming.

The other method has no common name, and will be called "dip coating." Here a heated object or mold is dipped into the powder, generally suspended in air. The object is so hot that particles coming in contact with it stick and melt,, gradually building up a coating. Again, depending on pretreatment of the surface, the coating will either adhere, or be removable.

Cylindrical objects of considerable size may be centrifugally cast. Polyethylene granules are placed in a heated cylinder or mold which is slowly rotated until the polyethylene is molten. The cylinder or mold is then rotated rapidly until the polyethylene is evenly distributed over the wall, and then cooled while still rotating to set the polyethylene.

An alternate method is to deliver molten polyethylene from an extruder to the rotating mold. In centrifugal casting it is generally necessary to maintain an inert atmosphere, usually nitrogen over the polyethylene to reduce oxidation.

For the production of models, prototypes, etc., polyethylene can be easily worked with wood or metal working tools. Heavy rod or block can be turned, planed, bored, shaped or any other machine tool operation can be performed, provided certain precautions are taken. Tools must be very sharp, cuts must be small, and speeds slow to prevent overheating. Cooling should be good.

Heat Sealing. The process of heat sealing is quite different from the above processing methods, but very important to the use of polyethylene. The absence of any satisfactory adhesive for polyethylene makes its heat sealability of paramount importance. Fortunately, it is easy to heat-seal polyethylene. The heated bar sealer is the commonest method used to make and close film bags. The material being sealed is clamped between two bars, one or both of which will be heated by electric resistance heaters. "Teflon"-coated glass cloth is often used to prevent sticking. When the plastic has been heated to fusion temperatures it is released. Since the sealed part is released hot, and the heat for fusion has to travel through the plastic to reach the sealing point, this method is limited to thin films.

One of the most satisfactory ways of heat sealing heavier sheets is the blow-torch method, in which two sheets are clamped together with a little of the edge of both sheets sticking out of the clamp. A gas flame is passed over the edges, melting them and forming a seal. Polyethylene collapsible tubes are commonly sealed in this way. Heat can also be furnished by radiant heaters.

The impulse method is closely related to the simple bar seal but can be used on heavier sheet. In this method the pieces are held in a clamp consisting of a resilient jaw and a cooled metal jaw. Between the cooled jaw and the plastic is an electric resistance wire. When the clamp is closed a short surge or impulse of electricity passes through the resistance wire to melt the plastic. The plastic is then held in the clamp until it is cooled by conduction to the cold bar. This prevents distortion at the seal and reduces squeeze out of material resulting in a stronger seal. The clamp bars are covered with "Teflon" covered glass tape to prevent sticking. An impulse sealer is shown in Figure 5-14.

Except for the simple bar seal, which may be any shape, the above methods are generally limited to straight line seals.

(*Courtesy Vertrod Corp.*)
Figure 5–14. Impulse-type heat-sealing machine.

One method for circular seals, useful only for fairly heavy sections, is frictional welding. In this process one of the pieces to be joined is held stationary, while the other is rotated rapidly. The pieces are pressed together and the friction melts the plastic at the point of contact. Rotation is then stopped and the assembly is pressed together until it sets.

Figure 5–15. Electronic type machine for treating polyethylene film to make it printable. (*Courtesy Modern Plastic Machinery Corp.*)

Cementing of polyethylene is not generally too satisfactory but a suitable bond for light service can be made using pressure-sensitive adhesives.

Printing on untreated polyethylene surface is generally unsatisfactory but excellent ink adhesion can be obtained when the surface is modified. There are a number of methods used. For film and sheet the most satisfactory method is to pass an electric discharge over the surface of the polyethylene. The next most common method is to subject the surface to an open gas flame. The body of the plastic is protected against overheating by running it over a water-cooled roller. Overtreatment in either method can cause cracking of the plastic and loss of heat-sealability. Figure 5-15 shows an electronic treating machine.

For irregular shapes not easily adapted to these methods there are several chemical processes, including wet oxidation with chromic acid solution and treatment with chlorine gas in the presence of ultraviolet light. Numerous patents exist for other chemical methods but they are not in general use.

This by no means exhausts the methods used for working polyethylene but it does cover the most important processes. Practically any technique employed in the plastic industry has at one time or another been used for polyethylene, and many combinations of methods are used for particular articles, but space does not permit an exhaustive study here.

6. FILM AND COATING APPLICATIONS OF POLYETHYLENE

Since the basis for the acceptance of any material for a given application is largely economic, it is necessary to understand the economic basis for the use of polyethylene film. While there are a few applications for which only polyethylene will do, and many where it is the best possible material regardless of cost, polyethylene is generally used because it is the cheapest material available for a given purpose.

The concept of polyethylene costing 35¢ a pound as a raw material being cheap, is hard to understand at first, but the reason is that it is cheap as a film or coating. An application requiring an extremely small amount of polyethylene may require more of a less expensive material. Just to give some idea of where polyethylene film fits into the economic picture, comparisons will be made. Since prices change rapidly, these figures cannot be up to date, but conditions in the industry at present would seem to indicate that comparisons will tend to be more, rather than less favorable to polyethylene as time goes on.

When polyethylene film first became available in a sufficient quantity to be considered seriously as a packaging material, it was relatively expensive, and could be sold only on the basis of extra value. However, aggressive pricing policies and the efficiency of increased production rapidly brought the price down. The first major landmark was the point where it became the cheapest transparent wrapping material. This meant that all the cellophane markets were open to polyethylene if it could do an adequate job. The present price structure was briefly mentioned in Chapter 2, but it is believed that it merits further discussion. At present, polyethylene film 1.5 mil, 18 inches or wider, costs 53¢ a pound against 61¢ for cellophane. This, however, does not by any means tell the whole story. The low specific gravity of polyethylene gives it a great deal more area per pound than cellophane. Therefore, if we change our pricing basis to an area of 1000 square inches of 1-mil film, we find polyethylene costs $.018 compared to $.031 for cellophane, or 59 per cent of the cost of cellophane.

Initially, such a comparison would have been just as misleading as the per pound price because equal thicknesses of cellophane and polyethylene were not competitive. Cellophane .00088 inch thick was competing with polyethylene .0015 inch thick bringing the price of equal areas back near to equality. This near equality was, however, adequate stimulus to put polyethylene to numerous packaging uses.

Recent developments have been toward thinner and thinner polyethylene films. The strength of polyethylene is quite adequate for many purposes, even below one-half mil, which gives sufficient protection for many purposes.

Until recently, two factors prevented the use of polyethylene films below one mil thickness—it was hard to extrude film that thin, and the resultant film was so limp and clinging that it was impracticable. Technological developments in resin manufacture, and in the art of film extrusion have now eliminated both of these obstacles. Longer extruders with improved screw and die designs make the production of half-mil polyethylene film entirely practicable. The availability of higher density resins producing a stiffer film with a harder surface has made it possible to produce half-mil film with reasonably good handling characteristics.

Even if operating difficulties keep the price of half-mil film at its present level of 80¢ per pound—and it seems unlikely that this will continue to be the case very long—the price of half-mil polyethylene on an area basis is remarkably low, about 1.3¢ per 1000 square inches, or less than 3¢ per yard of 60-inch wide material. Since it appears likely that both the resin and the processing technology will be further improved, this price will almost certainly be reduced in the near future.

It is evident that polyethylene film has not only far outdistanced cellophane as the cheapest available transparent packaging material, but that it is well on its way to being the cheapest wrapping or packaging material of any kind.

In many applications some of which will be discussed here, price is the really significant factor. Sometimes price merely determines that the job will be done using polyethylene rather than some other material. In many cases the low price of polyethylene is the factor that makes it possible to do the job at all.

In the following discussion an attempt has been made to keep in mind the powerful economic factors that underlie the present widespread uses of polyethylene. Polyethylene film has its largest application in the packaging field, and it has been most successful for packaging fresh produce. A major film producer estimates that 75 per cent of all polyethylene film is for consumer packaging and that at least 75 per cent of this is used for produce.

For many years fresh produce was an exception to the trend toward prepackaging in the food field. There were numerous reasons for this—the items varied in size and shape, they were sensitive to damage by the packaging machinery, and the consumer desired to see the product. The short shelf-life of the products was also a barrier because it introduced another operation which delayed getting the product from producer to consumer.

The main advantages of polyethylene prepackaging of produce items are:

(1) Reduction of waste or spoilage
(2) Convenience to the retailer
(3) Convenience to the consumer
(4) Opportunity for the promotion of brand names.

In many cases, the reduction in waste alone will pay for the packaging. Carrots were one of the first produce items to be packaged in polyethylene. A report from the U. S. Department of Agriculture* made the following observations.

Non-packaged bunch carrots were salable a much shorter period than prepackaged carrots because of the wilting of the tops and shrivelling of the roots. Weight loss of the carrots in polyethylene bags was less than 1 per cent after two days at 70 degrees, two weeks at 40 degrees, or three weeks at 32 degrees.

No decay developed on the topped prepackaged carrots at 40 or 32° F during the tests; however, some bacterial soft rot and mold were found after six days at 70 degrees. Tops should be completely cut off before carrots are prepackaged, since the tops, even when clipped to 1 inch, were the first part to show darkening, dying, sprouting or decay.

Polyethylene bags should be ventilated to prevent develop-

---

* Packaging carrots in different types of consumer bags by Hardenburg, Liebman & Schomer U.S.D.A. 1953.

ment of off-odor and off-flavor. This can be done by perforating the bags with four to eight one-quarter or one-eighth inch diameter holes. These bags were especially suitable because of their strength and moisture-proofness.

Similar advantages have been shown for a variety of other produce items. Figure 6-1 shows a number of produce items packaged in polyethylene bags.

Figure 6–1. Produce packed in polyethylene bags.
(*Courtesy Visking Corp.*)

Next to the saving in waste, convenience to the retailer was perhaps the greatest impetus to polyethylene packaging of produce. The self-service revolution in food retailing had enormously increased the efficiency of the grocery store, except at the produce counter, where the necessity for individually weighing and packaging each item still delayed service and increased sales costs. Prepackaging not only permits the rapid and efficient packaging and weighing of the produce but it enables the customer to serve himself. It also prevents the accumulation of "picked over" items that generally appear when self-service is permitted from bulk bins.

Although a great deal of produce packaging is still done at the individual retail store, the trend is to centralize it at a warehouse or even at the farm where the larger volume will permit the use of more efficient machinery and methods.

The advantages to the customer of prepackaging in polyethylene are:

(1) the product is fresher and in better condition; (2) it is cleaner because it has been protected from dust and airborne dirt and from handling; (3) the item is visible and can be examined through the wrapper; (4) the package is waterproof and thus protects other articles from moisture; (5) the package can be used not only to protect the remainder of the produce but also for other purposes.

These advantages have caused rapid dealer and consumer acceptance of prepackaging, and there is little doubt that the trend will not continue.

Table 6-1, taken from an article by D. R. Stokes, U. S. Department of Agriculture, gives some estimates on present and future produce packaging of some representative crops. It can be seen that, while a few crops such as carrots and radishes are already prepackaged to a large extent, most produce items are not. The estimated potential column indicates that this situation is not expected to continue, and that ultimately most produce will be prepackaged. From present indications polyethylene will be used for most of this.

TABLE 6–1. ESTIMATED POLYETHYLENE FILM USE IN PRODUCE PACKAGING

Crop	Avg. Ann. Supply (1948-53) M Lbs.*	Estimated % Now Packaged*	Unit Size	Estimated Potential Packaged
Apples	3790	25	3# 5# 8#	75
Beans (snap)	556	5	1# 2#	50
Beets	127	20	2#	75
Carrots	1749	80	1#	90
Grapefruit	1556	10	2# 3 ea. 4# 6 ea.	50
Grapes	1200	3	2#	50
Lemons	600	15	1# 6 ea.	50
Onions (dry)	1570	20	2# 4#	75
Oranges	4260	20	4# 1 doz.	50
Parsnips	34	25	2#	75
Peas	80	5	1#	50
Peppers (sweet)	340	5	1# 4 ea.	25
Potatoes	14920	35	3# 5# 10#	85
Radishes	162	50	½#	90
Sweet potatoes	890	1	3# 4#	85
Tangerines	281	5	3# 1 doz.	50

* Source: Produce Packaging Potential, D. R. Stokes, U.S.D.A.

Polyethylene is also widely used to protect produce during shipment. Its earliest use was for the banana shroud—a large bag put over a whole stalk of bananas before shipment. Polyethylene used for this purpose is bought in rolls of flat tubing 26 to 28 inches in diameter. It is shipped to the packing house in the country where the bananas are grown, and cut to the desired length.

When a stem of bananas is picked, it is shipped by rail to the packing house where it is washed in a mild acid bath. The shroud is then slipped over the stalk of bananas in much the same manner as a sock is put on. Knots are tied in the corners to prevent the sleeve from slipping off, leaving an opening at both the top and bottom for ventilation. The stalk of bananas then goes through the normal distribution cycle to the terminal ripening room.

This shroud costs about 15¢ per stem in materials and labor. The cost is justified by three factors:

(1) Moisture loss of the fruit is retarded. This means that the stem remains stiffer and the fingers stand out giving the stalk a better appearance. The color of the banana is also brighter, and the texture of the flesh is improved. The reduction in weight loss itself may pay for the shroud.

(2) Reduction of scars and bruises. The film acts as a scuff barrier and reduces the damage in transit caused by one item rubbing against another. The moisture retention, by stiffening the stalk, also helps to prevent the individual bananas from rubbing against each other.

(3) Acceleration of ripening. The shrouds shorten the normal ripening schedule by about 24 hours. This reduces the number of bananas that have to be in transit or in storage to meet a given shipping schedule, and also gives a certain flexibility to the ripening schedule in that the shrouds can be removed at the terminal ripening room to retard ripening. The ripening inside a shroud is more uniform than on an

Figure 6–2. Banana stalk wrapped in polyethylene.
(*Courtesy Visking Corp.*)

unprotected stalk. Figure 6-2 shows a stalk of wrapped bananas.

Figure 6–3. Polyethylene lined fruit crates.
(*Courtesy Bemis Brothers Bag Co.*)

Apples and pears also benefit from polyethylene protection during storage and shipping. A plastic film liner is placed inside the standard crate (Figure 6-3); this reduces moisture loss and shriveling of the fruit. Table 6-2 shows results on Anjou Pears. The most important gain is given in the last column, which shows that after ripening the pears packed in polyethylene remain salable for a longer time, thus reducing retailer losses.

TABLE 6–2. RIPENING OF ANJOU PEARS AT 65°F AFTER STORAGE AT 31° WHEN SEALED IN POLYETHYLENE OR PACKED IN THE STANDARD WAY, 1950*

Kind of Pack	Period of Cold Storage (days)	Period Ripened Under Seal (days)	Period to Acquire Optimum Dessert Quality (days)	Additional Period of Acceptable Dessert Quality (days)
Polyethylene	(152	(4	8	9
		7	10	7
	214	4	10	5
		7	11	2
Standard pack	152	0	8	4
	214	0	7	0

* Film liners for boxes of pears and apples, Gerhardt and Schower, USDA, January, 1954.

The use of plastic film is recommended when the crop is intended for late storage, and then only for sound fruit that has been washed with an effective fungicide since the high relative humidity inside the bag or box liner increases the possibility of decay.

Table 6-3 compares the maximum storage life of pears in the standard pack with some in sealed bags. It can be seen that pears keep longer when sealed.

TABLE 6–3. STORAGE LIFE OF FOUR VARIETIES OF PEARS AT 31°F WHEN PACKED IN STANDARD WAY AND IN SEALED FILM BAGS OR BOX LINERS*

Variety	Maximum Storage Life in Standard Pack (days)	Maximum Storage Life in Sealed Film Bags (days)
Bartlett	70- 85	107-126
Anjou	175-185	214-216
Comice	90-105	120-135
Bosc	90-100	120-130

* Source: *Ibid.*

Another advantage of the polyethylene bag, shown in Table 6-4, is consumer acceptance. This was a marketing test made for potatoes. It can be seen that the potatoes packaged in polyethylene bags outsold those in mesh bags, even against an appreciable price differential.

TABLE 6–4. CONSUMER ACCEPTANCE OF POLYETHYLENE AND MESH WINDOW PAPER BAGS AND CORRUGATED BOXES IN TWO BANGOR SUPERMARKETS FOR A SIX-WEEK PERIOD, 1952-53 SEASON*

	Type of 10-Pound Package		
	Polyethylene Bag	Mesh Window Bag	Corrugated Box
First 2-week period, Dec. 8-20			
Retail price per 10 lb. pkg.	$ 0.59	$ 0.59	$ 0.59
Per cent of test sales	63.5	25.7	10.8
Second 2-week period, Dec. 22-Jan. 3			
Retail price per 10 lb. pkg.	$ 0.57	$ 0.55	$ 0.59
Per cent of test sales	62.3	33.3	4.4
Third 2-week period, Jan. 5-16			
Retail price per 10 lb. pkg.	$ 0.59	$ 0.55	$ 0.59
Per cent of test sales	54.0	40.6	5.4

Source: Plastic Bags for Potato Packages, Maine Agr. Exp. Station, U. of Maine, Orono, Maine, May, 1953.

Table 6-5 shows the results of packaging green beans in polyethylene. In comparison with unpackaged beans, it can be seen that the decrease in weight loss alone might nearly pay for the cost of packaging, without any consideration of the improved quality and convenience.

TABLE 6–5. WEIGHT LOSSES FROM GREEN BEANS PACKAGED IN 14-OZ. POLYETHYLENE BAGS WITH VARIOUS TYPES AND NUMBERS OF PERFORATIONS AND DISPLAYED IN A SINGLE LAYER FOUR DAYS AT 65°F AND 67 TO 70 PER CENT RELATIVE HUMIDITY*

	Polyethylene 150		
Number of Perforations	¼-inch holes	⅛-inch holes	⅛-inch flaps
0	0.6	0.6	—
2	0.8	0.8	—
4	1.8	0.8	—
8	2.8	1.3	0.8
16	3.4	1.5	1.0
32	5.9	2.9	1.4

* Weight losses from similar sized units of non-packaged beans averaged 19.3 per cent in the same period. A bushel hamper of beans lost 7.9 per cent in weight.
Source: Pre-Pack-Age, Vol. 7, No. 6, February, 1954.

Table 6-6 is a composite list of all fruits and vegetables which were reported as being prepackaged for consumer sale (during 1952) from a U. S. Department of Commerce Survey. While no detailed statistics are available as to percentages now packed, or expected to be packed, it can be seen that these items represent a large potential application for polyethylene film.

TABLE 6–6

Apples	Collards	Mustard Greens
Apricots	Corn	Onions
Asparagus	Cranberries	Oranges
Bananas	Endives	Peas
Beets	Garlic	Plums
Blueberries	Grapes	Potatoes
Broccoli	Grapefruit	Potatoes, peeled
Brussels Sprouts	Greenbeans	Radishes
Cabbage	Kale	Spinach
Carrots	Lemons	Salad
Cauliflower	Lettuce	Squash, diced
Celery	Lima Beans	Strawberries
Cherries	Limes	Tomatoes
Cloves	Mushrooms	

Meats

Polyethylene is extensively used for packaging fresh and processed meats. As mentioned previously, polyethylene has a unique combination of impermeability to water and permeability to gases. This permits the development of attractive bloom on red meats, and prevents the development of off-odors and flavor in poultry, and at the same time it prevents moisture loss.

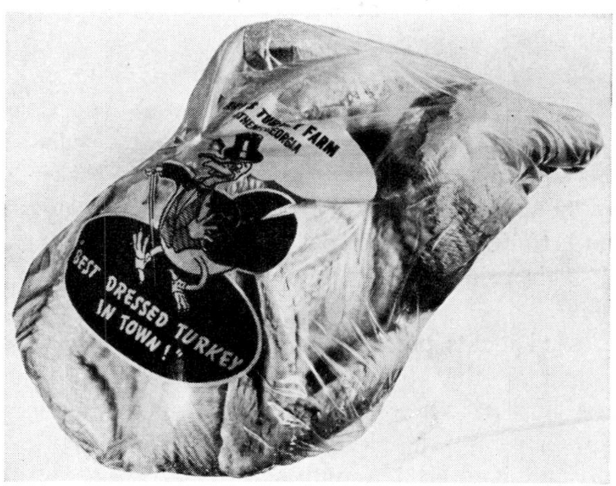

Figure 6–4. Turkey wrapped in polyethylene film. (*Courtesy Visking Corp.*)

Although a great deal of meat is still hand wrapped by the retail butcher, the packaging operation is reverting to the packer level for greater efficiency. In order to package irregularly shaped pieces, such as whole poultry, polyethylene shrinkable film is used. Unlike other shrinkable film it does not require immersion in boiling water after packaging.

When packing poultry the bag is stretched tightly over a filling "horn" and the bird is pushed, breast first, into the bottom of the bag. The bag is pushed on through the horn; any air is then removed and the bag is tied off. The film shrinks slowly until the package fits tightly. Figure 6-4 shows a bird packaged in this manner.

A polyethylene film application that may not be considered strictly as film, because the package is completed at the extruder, has been developed in Denmark using an extrusion die somewhat similar to that for blown film. The die, which faces downward, is oval rather than round, and the center is hollow. Frozen fish at $-30°$ C are fastened at regular intervals to a thin cord and drawn through the hollow center of the die while the polyethylene is being extruded. The hot film conforms to the contours of the fish and makes an attractive package. The polyethylene is heat-sealed at the intervals and cut apart in the sealed portion. This is a quick and economical method of packaging large quantities of fish, and trade marks or descriptive labels are easily included. This principle should have wide application in food packaging.

Processed meats present a slightly different problem from fresh meat in that the oxygen transmission of the polyethylene has an adverse effect on the appearance of the product, causing browning or fading. As a result of this, polyethylene is used in combination with cellophane. Dry cellophane is an excellent barrier to oxygen and carbon dioxide, but the presence of moisture greatly increases its permeability. By using polyethylene on the inside for water resistance, and cellophane outside, the best properties of both materials are retained. The package most generally used for this purpose is a pouch formed by sealing two pieces of laminate together at the edges. In most cases, an envelope is first made by sealing three sides, the meat is then inserted and the fourth side is sealed to complete the package. The package may be evacuated before sealing for maximum protection, but this is not necessary unless long storage is anticipated. Since processed meats also fade from light exposure a large printed label is frequently used to shield the product from the light.

In large installations the pouches may be formed directly from roll stock as they are used. The following notes on Wilson & Company's Oklahoma City operation on luncheon meats will give an idea of how a large modern plant works.

The food product is sliced, weighed and placed on a feed conveyor. The wrapping, vacuumizing, and sealing are carried out without further manual handling, at a rate of 40 packages per minute. The package is formed directly on the machine from imprinted cellophane roll stock having an extrusion coating of 2 mils of polyethylene. It is claimed that a saving of up to 60 per cent may be realized by using roll stock. Labor costs are at a minimum since only one operator is required on a machine.

The cellophane-polyethylene film is taken from the parent roll by feed rollers, and shaped by wrapping it around a forming tube. The product is then automatically deposited in the tube and a rotary sealer makes the lengthwise seal. Conveyor belts carry the tubed product across a folding plate which folds the film up against the package. A sealing head tucks the sides of the package and crimp seals about 75 per cent of the length at each end. A short conveyor belt then carries the package to a cutting head which cuts it to the desired length and deposits it in a tucking unit which places it directly under a vacuum chamber. Here the air is exhausted and the final end seal is made. As the packs emerge from the vacuum chamber they are transferred to a conveyor which delivers them from the side of the machine. Wilson uses a facsimile thermoplastic label to identify the product, but the machine can also be equipped to use preprinted wrap materials.

The polyethylene coated disposable baby diaper is interesting because the polyethylene is not merely a waterproofing material. The polyethylene is coated over a pile of loose highly absorbent cellulose fibers. The film of polyethylene holds this together in pad form and also seals the pad to the backing fabric. In addition to this, the polyethylene acts as an adhesive to hold two reinforcing strips at the edges of the assembly. These strips can be pinned without tearing. The soft fabric-and-pulp lining functions as a diaper that absorbs up to 15 times its own weight in water; the outer coating of polyethylene takes the place of the usual baby pants and provides hold-together strength, water and chemical resistance, and a pliant, soft surface texture. About one-tenth the weight of the lightest cloth diaper, it folds so compactly that a day's supply will fit in a handbag and after use, it can be disposed of in a trash can.

Some of the most unique and interesting packaging applications of polyethylene depend on the high oxygen and carbon dioxide transmission of the film, which makes it possible for live plants to live for a considerable period completely sealed in a polyethylene bag. This is causing a revolution in the marketing of plants, because it is now possible to prepackage plants at the grower, and be sure of their arrival in good condition weeks later. In one test, plants were still growing and in good shape ten weeks after packaging. The polyethylene prevents moisture loss, so that watering is unnecessary. It is, however, necessary to expose the package to light. Less revolutionary but still important, is the use of polyethylene to wrap the roots of plants shipped in a dormant condition. The moisture retention and oxygen transmission of the polyethylene keep the roots in good condition for a long time.

Perhaps the most surprising of all packaging uses is the

practice of shipping live fish in polyethylene bags. The fish, with an adequate water supply, are placed in a bag, which is tied shut and shipped in a corrugated board carton. This makes a light, inexpensive shipping container which has proved to be very durable. Figure 6-5 shows fish being packed. In this case, the fish are tropical so the carton has a liner of thermal insulation to prevent chilling.

Figure 6–5. Live fish packed in polyethylene bags. (*Courtesy Spencer Chemical Co.*)

The same technique is widely used for shipping liquids in fiber drums. A polyethylene film liner is placed in the drum and it is then filled and closed tightly. The closure is made with a separate disc of polyethylene. These containers are cheaper than metal drums; and they are resistant to many chemicals that would ordinarily corrode metal. Material with a delicate odor or flavor that would be contaminated by metal can safely be shipped in these. Such liners are also used in metal drums to protect either the drum or its contents.

An interesting European application involves the use of polyethylene-coated cardboard, where the polyethylene acts both as a moisture barrier, and as a means of sealing the package. "Tetra-pak" is a container for liquids which is made continuously from a flat sheet, and filled during manufacture. The basic principle is shown in Figure 6-6.

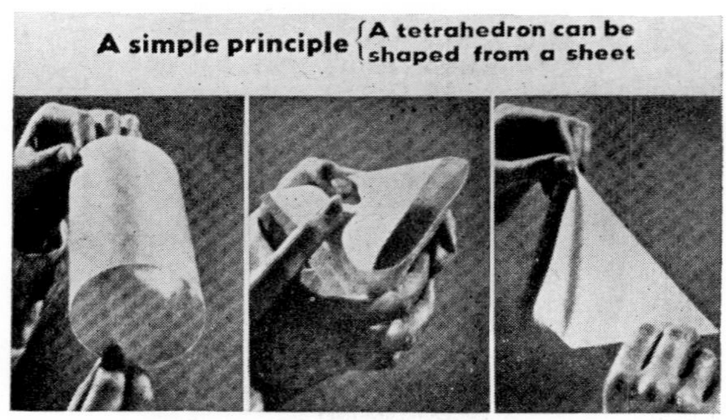

Figure 6–6. The principle of "Tetra-pak." (*Courtesy Tetra-pak Co.*)

The sheet is first shaped into a cylinder by means of a single lengthwise seal. The ends of the cylinder are then flattened along perpendicular axes and sealed forming a tetrahedral container.

The sequence of operation is shown in Figure 6-7 and is described below:

(1) The polyethylene coated paper, which arrives at the dairy in a tightly wrapped reel to protect the inner surface from contamination, is sterilized by passing it over an electric element.

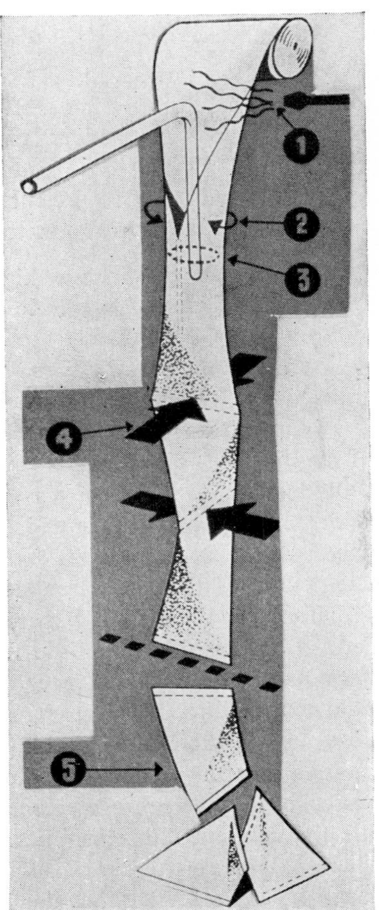

Figure 6–7. "Tetra-pak" sequence of operations.
(*Courtesy Tetra-pak Co.*)

(2) The paper is formed into a tube, the seam of which is heat-sealed.

(3) The tube is filled with milk to a constant level, the filling pipe ending below the surface of the liquid.

(4) The tetrahedrons are formed and sealed by pairs of electrically heated jaws operating under pressure and at right-angles to each other.

(5) The ribbon of filled cartons is cut into separate Tetra-pak containers ready for distribution to retailers.

These operations are performed on a highly developed automatic machine which requires very little attention once it is set up.

One of the major advantages of the Tetra-pak is its ease of storage and transportation. By reason of their novel shape, filled Tetra-paks require little space, and moreover, they are designed to fit snugly into special hexagonal galvanized baskets, which will take three layers of six each. They can be stacked on and alongside each other to insure maximum utilization of space.

It should be remembered that storage space is at a premium in most dairies. The reels of paper, sufficient for thousands of Tetra-paks, require very little floor space. As the paper used for making Tetra-paks is coated with polyethylene at a high temperature, it is automatically sterilized during production, and is therefore suitable for packaging food products. As an extra precaution, the polyethylene coated paper passes over an electric element which makes the surface sterile the moment filling commences.

The unique shape of the Tetra-pak makes it easy to handle. It can be set down on any side, without danger of leakage, and takes up very little room in the refrigerator or market basket. It is easily opened by cutting off a corner, and the partly empty carton can be reclosed simply by folding over the cut place.

An important advantage of Tetra-pak over glass milk bottles is the fact that it protects the contents from exposure to light, which results in off-flavor and loss of vitamins. The following is quoted from work reported by Sonja Mattison of the State Dairy Research Station, Alnarp, Sweden:

"In the present paper an account is given of a comparison between milk packed in clear glass bottles and milk packed in Tetra-pak, with respect to the decomposition of ascorbic acid and the development of so-called sunlight flavor on exposure of the bottle or carton to sunlight or diffuse daylight.

"The investigation showed that 70% of the ascorbic acid disappeared from the glass bottled milk after 10 minutes of exposure to sunlight, whereas only 8% to 15% of the ascorbic acid had disappeared from the Tetra-pak milk after exposure to sunlight for one hour; that 70% to 85% of the ascorbic acid had disappeared after 6 hours of exposure to diffuse daylight, whereas only 0% to 10% had disappeared from Tetra-pak milk; that sunlight flavor appears in glass bottled milk after exposure to sunlight for 2 minutes or after exposure to diffuse daylight for 2 hours, and in Tetra-pak milk after exposure to sunlight for 20 to 30 minutes, while after exposure to diffuse daylight for 6 hours, Tetra-pak milk has still not acquired any sunlight flavor.

"Consequently, Tetra-pak affords a very good, even if not complete protection for the milk against the development of sunlight flavor and against the light-induced decomposition of ascorbic acid."

The Use of Polyethylene in Hardware Packaging

The self-service trend in retailing encouraged the development of a wide variety of consumer packages for hardware. The requirements here differed somewhat from those in the produce trade. Protection from moisture and from the effects of handling is important. Visibility of the product is also a major factor but the two most important factors are the durability of the package under conditions of use and its low cost. Figure 6-8 shows hardware packaged in polyethylene bags.

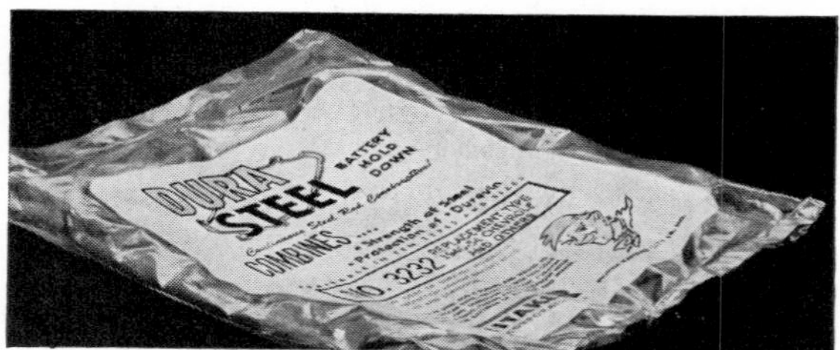

Figure 6–8. Hardware packaged in a polyethylene bag. (*Courtesy Spencer Chemical Co.*)

There are many items in the hardware trade for which the unit cost is necessarily small, and the many ingenious packages devised for packaging them are all out of proportion to the total sale. A small polyethylene bag costs only a fraction of a cent, and several ingenious automatic packaging machines have been devised which fill and seal the bags at a high rate of speed. Figure 6-9 shows a bag-making and filling machine used for this purpose. The machine can use preprinted polyethylene to brand and identify the product, or a card can be inserted with the product. By using a bag with a hole near one end, it can be hung on display racks for easy selection by the customer.

A more impressive, but also more expensive, polyethylene package for hardware is the so-called "skin pack." The article is laid on a printed card, which is either polyethylene coated,

Figure 6–9. Machine to make, fill, and seal polyethylene bags. (*Courtesy Mercury Heat Sealing Equipment Co.*)

or coated with a thermoplastic cement that will bond polyethylene. Unless it is quite small, the card is also perforated. The assembly is laid on a wire mesh or other porous support over a box that can be evacuated. A polyethylene film usually .004 or .005 inch thick is clamped in a frame above this, heated by radiation from an electric heater, and when properly softened, it is brought down over the article and the card. Immediately after this vacuum is drawn forming the plastic closely around the article and the card. The article is fastened firmly to the card, but is completely visible and stands out in such a way as to attract attention. This makes a very strong, tough package, which is attractive to the consumer. It is frequently made with other films but in applications where low cost and durability are important, polyethylene is often the choice. This is particularly true with sharp or irregular objects, since polyethylene shows superior puncture resistance.

The packaging of toys in polyethylene bags has become almost a standard practice. The transparent bag permits the toy to be examined and even felt without soiling. The rack display technique mentioned previously is extensively used for small toys, and greatly increases the efficiency of counter space. The bag makes a good multiple unit package and if a card is inserted to increase the size of the package, it is an inexpensive and effective antipilferage device for small items. In self-service stores, pilferage is a particularly serious problem with small toy items. Increasing the sales unit is an old device for improving retailing efficiency. Most methods of packaging add so much to the cost of the article that this device has heretofore been limited to toys of considerable value. The polyethylene bag is a cheap and convenient way to assemble "sets" or "kits" consisting of small items.

Figure 6-10 shows an interesting package that also serves as a dispenser. The dispensing feature adds little or nothing to the cost of what is otherwise a conventional 1½-mil polyethylene bag. Part way up the bag, or tube, just below the rim of the bottom cup in the nested stack, a slight construction is formed by a rounded heat seal on each side just as a "pinch" extending no more than ¼-inch in from the edge.

Two spot heat seals placed opposite each other, near the end of an open bag, constrict the bag just enough to permit

Figure 6–10. Combination paper cup container and dispenser. (*Courtesy Lily Cup Co.*)

one cup to be pulled out at a time while others stay put. A stapled die-cut header provides identity and hang-up tab.

Polyethylene film is one of the best moisture barriers or "membranes" available to the building trade. There is practically no place in a building where a moisture barrier is needed, where polyethylene cannot be used. As the effectiveness and economy of the material gain recognition, it undoubtedly will be incorporated in many places where heretofore effective moisture-proofing was too expensive. In order to eliminate the problem of seams many manufacturers produce extremely wide film for the building trades.

Perhaps the simplest use for polyethylene film in the building trade is to cover the earth in the "crawl space" under houses where the foundation is not excavated. The polyethylene not only prevents moisture evaporation from the ground, which may cause floors to buckle, beams to rot and pipes to rust but it also reduces the amount of dust, dirt and insects entering the house from this source. Figure 6-11 shows such an installation being made in a finished house.

Figure 6–11. Polyethylene film being used to reduce moisture transmission from a basement crawl space.
(*Courtesy Spencer Chemical Co.*)

If polyethylene is laid under a concrete floor slab, or outside a foundation wall, it is possible to make a really waterproof house. If it is anticipated that there will be actual water pressure against the membrane, joints between the sheets should be sealed with a cold cut back floor adhesive. Eleven hundred square feet of polyethylene—a good average figure for underhouse areas—costs about $15.00 and one man can lay it in about an hour and a half. The plastic film, when installed, gives virtually 100 per cent protection against underhouse moisture vapor.

When a wooden floor is laid over a concrete slab, a perfect moisture barrier is essential or the floor will warp. Standard practice for this has been a hot mopped membrane of asphalt saturated felt. It has been found that just as good results can be obtained using two-mil polyethylene held down by a cold cut-back floor adhesive, at a cost in labor and materials between a quarter and an eighth that of the hot mopped membrane.

Figure 6–12. Polyethylene film laid over wet concrete. (*Courtesy Visking Corp.*)

When polyethylene film is used inside the forms in a cast concrete foundation, it facilitates removal of the forms, increases their life, and waterproofs the foundation as well.

If a sheet of polyethylene is laid over a slab of concrete while it is drying, it will promote even cure by retaining moisture, and will eliminate the need to re-wet the concrete in hot weather. Figure 6-12 shows how this is done.

Polyethylene also makes an inexpensive and extremely effective covering to protect building materials stored on the job from getting wet (Figure 6-13).

Figure 6–13. Polyethylene film used as tarpaulin to protect building materials stored on the job. (*Courtesy Visking Corp.*)

The use of polyethylene film to enclose scaffoldings (Figure 6-14) and incomplete structures frequently makes it possible to continue work during periods of inclement weather. Its transparency makes it light and pleasant to work inside the enclosure whereas canvas or other temporary walls would make it dark and difficult.

Inexpensive temporary storm windows can be made by tacking polyethylene film on the inside of window frames. If the windows leak it may be necessary to use a light frame to hold the polyethylene tightly to the window frame.

Polyethylene film is one of the best ways to moistureproof the walls and the roof of a house. It prevents the accumulation of moisture in the insulation during cold weather, and by keeping the wall space dry it prevents paint blistering and deterioration of the house structure. When

Figure 6–14. Polyethylene film used to enclose scaffolding. (*Courtesy Spencer Chemical Co.*)

polyethylene film is used for this purpose, it is stapled to the warm side of the rafters and studding before the interior wall is put up. It may be used vertically in narrow widths, in which case it is lapped the full width of the stud on alternate studs, or it may be obtained in full wall height widths and laid across the studs. Ceiling and floor laps should be about 6 inches and care must be taken to seal around junction boxes, pipes, outlets, etc., to maintain a good vapor barrier.

Uses of Polyethylene Film in the Home

Home uses of polyethylene stemmed from the re-use of bags originally obtained as packaging materials. These proved so useful that there is now a very considerable and growing retail market for polyethylene bags and sheeting.

Polyethylene bags are available in many sizes at most large department and variety stores, and many also stock sheeting. The large mail order houses all offer bags and sheeting. There are many uses but just a few of the more common ones will be mentioned here.

- Moth-proof garment bag
- Laundry bag for dirty clothes
- Wet diaper bag
- Bag to keep laundry damp for ironing
- Bag for garbage disposal
- Food storage bag especially in refrigerator or freezer
- Ice cube bag
- Bag to keep bread fresh
- Tobacco pouch

Sheeting also has a wide variety of home uses such as:

- Slip covers for furniture
- Covers to protect outdoor furniture
- Book jackets
- Phonograph record covers
- Covers for appliances
- Floor cover under baby's high chair
- Table cloth protectors
- Shelf and drawer liners
- Aprons
- Clothes hamper liners
- Wall cover wherever splashing on wall is possible
- Cigar box liner
- Mattress cover for baby beds
- Shower curtains

Closely related to these are its use on hunting or fishing trips:

Bags to bring home catch
Lunch bags
Ground cloth under sleeping bag
Cover to keep guns or other
  equipment dry
Emergency rain cape

This list could be extended almost indefinitely and as more people become acquainted with the film it will certainly find increasing uses around the home.

Agricultural Uses

The agricultural uses for polyethylene film are in their infancy, but once the material becomes known, they should expand rapidly. The main agricultural uses fall into the following categories:

(1) Mulches to conserve water and reduce weed growth.
(2) Seed bed covers.
(3) Greenhouses.
(4) Storage of harvested crops.

Mulches. Polyethylene film mulches differ from other film uses in that it is usually desirable in cool climates to use black film in order to shade out the weed growth and to preserve the film longer. In hot weather clear film destroys weeds rapidly. It is particularly advantageous where crops must be artificially irrigated because of the reduction in water evaporation. Polyethylene film is frequently used for mulching strawberry beds. It is laid in long, rather narrow strips over the area which is going to be planted and thoroughly weighted down by turning a furrow of earth over both edges.

The plants are then planted through slashes in the film. Alternatively, polyethylene may be laid over the plants which are permitted to grow under it until they blossom, when slashes are made and the polyethylene tucked under the plant. The advantages of this are cleaner berries and easier picking, although reduction of mold and rot is often the main purpose. Clear film is often used even if it does not give as good weed control as the black, because at the end of the usual three-year strawberry plant cycle, the clear film has decomposed to the point where it can be plowed under, while black film has to be removed from the field. If the plant is going to grow under the film for some time, evidently it must be clear. Figure 6-15 shows a field mulched with polyethylene film. Results from polyethylene film mulching vary extensively depending on the soil and the crop.

Figure 6–15. Polyethylene film used to mulch field of strawberries. (*Courtesy Spencer Chemical Co.*)

Seed Beds. Although the use of polyethylene film for greenhouses and cold frames has not yet become a major application, it has received a great deal of study. In Japan the largest use for polyethylene film is to cover seed beds. In the intensive agriculture of that country, the growth accelerated by the polyethylene cover at the beginning of the season sometimes permits an extra crop to be produced. Even if this is not the case, earlier and larger crops are produced.

It is possible to use polyethylene over seed beds merely by laying film over the prepared bed, and anchoring it firmly around the edges. This will retain heat and moisture, speed germination of the seeds and protect them from birds and from washing. On soils which have a tendency to "crust," the increased stand of plants under polyethylene compared to unprotected beds may be great. Film which is laid down must be removed before the seedlings get very big otherwise the whipping of the film in the wind will break the seedlings. Mere contact between film and leaf appears to do no harm.

A specialized seed-bed use for polyethylene (Figure 6-16) shows a method for repairing damaged or bare spots in a lawn. The bare spot is scratched up, seeded and watered, after which, a sheet of polyethylene is laid over the area and fastened down by driving 2-inch roofing nails, spaced about 6 inches apart, around the edge. The polyethylene cover is left on until the grass is long enough to be cut.

Perhaps the most important job of this miniature polyethylene greenhouse is to keep out the rain. Contrary to popular belief, rain is often grass' worst enemy, washing the seed away from the bald spot. But covered with polyethylene, the seed stays put. It won't wash away and the birds can't get to it, and, with adequate prewatering, as described above, the seedlings will water themselves. The polyethylene "green-

Figure 6–16. Polyethylene film used to protect new grass in a lawn. (*Courtesy Spencer Chemical Co.*)

house" makes its own rain as moisture evaporating from the ground condenses on the underside of the film and returns to the earth. Yet sunlight and air can get through, and instead of coming out of wraps looking pale and wan, the young grass is more likely to startle you with its vivid green color.

In Japan it is common practice to raise the film slightly above the soil, in which case it can be left on until the plants begin to crowd the sheet, thus permitting a longer period of accelerated growth. Low leafy crops like lettuce may advantageously be brought to maturity under it.

Greenhouses. The Agricultural Experiment Station of the University of Kentucky at Lexington, Kentucky, has done some very interesting work in greenhouses glazed entirely with polyethylene film. These houses make it possible to grow out-of-season crops much cheaper than in glass houses, because overhead and heating costs are greatly reduced. Figure 6-17 shows a polyethylene greenhouse.

Figure 6–17. A polyethylene greenhouse.
(*Courtesy Spencer Chemical Co.*)

Construction. The plastic is extended into the ground on the sides, hence, there are no side walls. The supporting 4″ x 4″ side posts and sash bars which go into the ground should be treated with wood preservatives. The plastic, however, lasts better under ground than above.

The eave plates and ridge bars are made of 2″ x 4″ lumber. The sash bars are 2″ x 2″ lumber. The angle at the eaves should be 40° instead of 33° (standard house) to aid in snow clearance. Removable side post supports should be used to hold up any snow which may accumulate on the roof.

Fastening the Plastic. It is best to run the plastic the long way. If the house is 84 feet long, 85 feet of the plastic is rolled on a pipe or stick 6 inches longer on each end than the plastic. One man tacks the plastic at one gable next to the top. The other rolls out 6 or 8 feet of plastic or enough to cover 3 or 4 sashbars, and pulls tightly on it. The other tacks the lath on down to within 8 inches of the lower edge. The next length is placed under the 8 inches forming a lap of about 6 inches, and this is tacked in the same way. If the lap is about 6 inches and the plastic is pulled tightly, it is unnecessary to seal the laps since they will stay together even in strong winds. The inside layer can be put up with paper disks and tacks since the wind does not get to it.

Cost Estimate. Since the project has started, the cost of plastic has dropped about 12 per cent. To cover an 18′ x 84′ house, the cost is only about $24 for the outside layer of 0.002 inch plastic and $15 for the inside layer of 0.0015 inch plastic. This is based on large quantity, wholesale prices. Plastic in small amounts costs more. The framework cost varies from $150 to $250. A blueprint for the 18′ x 84′ house is available through the Agricultural Engineering Department, University of Kentucky, Lexington, Kentucky, for 10 cents.

Heat and Moisture Retention. The heat build-up from the sun is not so great under plastic as under glass, but the heat loss at night is less. This is good for plants. With the double layer of plastic, the loss is less than half that with glass. This was determined by testing the Btu needed in a plastic house. It was found that 100,000 Btu kept the house at about 60° F when the outside temperature was 0° F. By standard methods of calculation, a glass house of the same size would require 200,000 Btu. It seems that the best insulation is obtained by maintaining about a 2-to-3-inch dead air space between the layers. If the space is much wider, convection currents cause losses; if it is much closer, there is not enough dead air to reduce heat radiation.

Moisture retention is much greater than with glass because plastic has no laps and is tighter, thus reducing the amount of watering needed. If the houses do not get air exchange, however, there is greater danger of disease. Ventilation and the application of fungicides are required.

Light Transmission. The light transmission of polyethylene film may be as much as 90 per cent of that of glass. However, the more ultraviolet light and heat there is, the quicker the plastic deteriorates. If installed in late September, it will hold up until the following June. Some new types are being tried which give promise of lasting longer, but as yet they are not available commercially.

Ventilation. So far, ventilation has been provided by side drop vents and by vents in the gable ends. The difficulty of the side vents is that drafts affect the plants. Since air exchange is important, it seems that ridge vents should be made. Of course, ordinary glass house machinery can be used, but this is expensive. Cheaper methods will be investigated shortly.

Another way of accomplishing air exchange is to use exhaust fans in connection with the heating system. These can be used to circulate the heat on cold nights and during the day, and on warm nights air can be pulled in from the outside and distributed without creating a draft on the plants. A comparison of this method with ridge vents will be investigated. Gable-end vents would be installed on all houses.

Heating. Because of its uniformity, the best heat is from hot-water fins. It is more uniform than steam or hot air. However, the initial cost is high and it requires more attention although the operation can be fully automatic.

For small units, gas heaters can be used which are entirely automatic and the initial cost is low. The heat units (Btu) from natural gas cost somewhat more than those from coal, and those from propane cost considerably more, but the handling of coal and ashes is costly on small units, as a result of which gas heaters are preferred.

If combustion is complete, propane gas gives off only CO_2 and water. If the CO_2 is not too concentrated, it helps plant growth. Propane can be used successfully if vents are provided. These do not have to be especially tight, allowing some CO_2 to escape. If natural gas is used, the vents should be tight because some types of natural gas are harmful to plants. Burners should be used that give complete combustion. Incomplete combustion gives off aldehydes and other products harmful to plants.

A new heat distributor duct made of pigmented polyethylene is attractive and it is much cheaper than pipe. Plain white plastic can be used, but it does not radiate too well. The first trial using polyethylene laminated aluminum at Lexington gave exceptionally good results. Tomato plants set along the outside grew in subzero weather because the soil as well as the air is warmed by this method. The ducts are made by placing wire wickets every 2 feet and covering them with plastic. The edges are made airtight with the soil. A blower forces the heat through this tunnel.

The following material is from a report by Professor E. M. Emmet at this station:

RESULTS WITH CROPS

(1) Bibb Lettuce: Bibb lettuce produced extra large and solid heads in much shorter time than usual. It seemed to thrive under the conditions in the plastic house, and its quality was very good.

(2) Leaf Lettuce: Grand Rapids lettuce grew well and was of good quality; just as good, if not better, than when grown under glass.

(3) Kentucky Wonder Bean: The plants grew vigorously. However, there was a tendency for them to vine and not set pods, especially if the concentration of nitrogen in the soil was high. If plenty of air was admitted and temperatures of 60° F. or more were maintained, a good set could be obtained. Plastic keeps the humidity too high if air exchange is not accomplished.

(4) Tomatoes: Tomatoes grown at the same time, under glass and plastic were compared. Here again, there was some tendency towards vegetation, but good fruiting occurred a little later than was true for fruit grown under glass. The fruits, though about a week later, were larger than when grown under glass and were of good quality. The yields have not been completed but appear to be about equal. There was some tendency towards rotting in the plastic house when air exchange was slow, but the glass house dried out much more rapidly and there was less rotting in it; however, there was more tendency for blossom-end rot to occur in the glass house. Blights did not seem to be worse, but there was some tendency for more leaf mold and sclerotinia rot in the plastic house. This is not bad if air exchange is kept up on all days possible. Fusarium wilt occurred in the glass house, but has not yet been seen in the plastic houses. This was explained on the basis that the plastic house was on fresh soil, while the glass house was on old tomato soil. However, fusarium later appeared in a new glass house located on new soil which had been in sod.

(5) Eggplant: Eggplant is quite sensitive to adverse conditions, but in a plastic house it grew and fruited even better than did tomatoes.

(6) Peppers: Peppers grew well.

(7) Cucumbers: No extensive tests have been made, but a few vines grew vigorously and set a good crop. There was not so much mildew as in the glass house.

(8) Beets: Beets showed some tendency to large tops, but grew vigorously.

(9) Cabbage: Cabbage grew vigorously and headed well.

(10) Flowers: About 10 different annual flowering plants have been tried in a small way and all did well.

While the foregoing report was from Kentucky, this does not necessarily indicate that the polyethylene greenhouse is better in moderate climates. As a matter of fact, the exact contrary is true; the main success of the polyethylene greenhouse has been in cold climates. A report by Jesse M. Rawson of the South Dakota Agricultural Experiment Station in Brookings, South Dakota, on a slight modification of the house described above, was very favorable. He reports that the house withstood 55 miles per hour winds without damage and concludes:

"The advantage of this house as we see it now, are low original cost, reasonable heating and maintenance costs, great flexibility, ability to withstand wind, snow, and hail, and the need for less frequent watering."

The polyethylene greenhouse is of great interest in the Scandanavian countries, particularly in Finland where a great deal of work has been done with them. The short growing season in these countries forces them to grow more things under glass than in this country and the savings effected using the polyethylene greenhouse are important.

Conditions there result in a somewhat different approach to the polyethylene greenhouse. Heavy snow loads and high winter winds require the outer layer to be made of a heavier plastic than we use—6 or 8 mil material is common. On the other hand, the short summer, with low ultraviolet ray concentrations, reduces the destructive action of sunlight on the film to such an extent that the greenhouse lasts 3 to 5 years before the sheeting must be replaced, which more than offsets the added cost of the heavier film. It can be seen from this that the plastic greenhouse has great possibilities all over the world.

Harvested Crops. The use of polyethylene film to protect harvested crops covers a wide range. It is one of the cheapest and lightest materials for use as a tarpaulin over haystacks or other crops to keep them dry. It is used as a silo liner to protect the silo from corrosion or rot caused by the wet contents. It is used as an inside cover to protect the top layer in a partly filled silo from the air. The importance of protecting silage from air is shown by a report of the South Dakota Experiment Station on Spoilage and Microorganisms in Alfalfa Silage. After a careful investigation of all the means available for the preservation of silage, including various additives and means of stacking, they conclude:

"The best way to produce good silage and cut down spoilage is to enclose the stack tightly with a durable plastic cover."

Polyethylene will protect a wide variety of crops from drying out during storage. Polyethylene bags will protect seeds from moisture and insects and will protect roots kept for replanting from drying out.

Tarpaulins made of polyethylene are useful as covers for soil, buildings, or equipment during fumigation because the polyethylene is resistant to most of the chemicals used.

Soil fumigation is an inexpensive and effective method of controlling weeds and insects, improving germination and providing healthy seedlings. Gas fumigation with methyl bromide or related gases has proved itself in nurseries, greenhouses, mushroom houses, and seed beds. Gas fumigants and tarpaulins made of polyethylene provide a quick, economical method of increasing yields, and effect a saving on seed cost through higher germination and fertilizer cost because seedlings rather than weeds utilize the fertilizer. Fumigation costs are more than recovered through increased yield.

Polyethylene tarpaulins are economical and durable in steam sterilizing. They have been used for the "buried conductor" and "Thomas" methods. The tarpaulin should be protected from direct contact with steam inlet pipes. Users have reported 50 steamings with tarpaulins made of polyethylene and the cover is still in good shape. It is not necessary to dry the tarpaulins before storing them.

Bagged grains and other commodities are economically fumigated using polyethylene tarpaulins. The merchandise can be covered in the warehouse and infestation eliminated on the spot, without the expense of removing it to fumigation chambers.

Polyethylene is also used to line irrigation ditches and ponds to prevent moisture loss. The availability of polyethylene film has made it possible to build ponds and reservoirs in locations where it was never before possible. In one location in Australia, a large dam was built nearly 20 years ago for a reservoir but it never filled because the soil did not hold water. Recently the bottom of the reservoir was carefully graded and completely lined with 4-mil polyethylene film, the laps being sealed with mastic cement. The plastic was covered with 6 inches of clay for mechanical protection and the reservoir now holds water for the first time. This technique makes it unnecessary to consider the bottom conditions when a reservoir is being planned since any sort of structure can now be made completely waterproof. This development may have a tremendous influence on control of our water resources.

7. APPLICATIONS OF POLYETHYLENE PIPE, COATED WIRE AND MISCELLANEOUS EXTRUSIONS

Chapter 2 discusses the physical properties of polyethylene pipe that first led to its use. Because of its inertness to solutions and atmospheres that are corrosive to metal pipe, its first use was in the chemical industry, particularly in electroplating. The usual electroplating shop has a tremendous corrosion problem and in many cases, where solution temperatures are not too high, the substitution of polyethylene pipe for metal saves a great deal of money.

One of the first large-volume uses for polyethylene pipe was for mine drainage. Mine waters are generally acid and rapidly destructive of steel piping. Polyethylene pipe is so durable in these applications that after its initial surge a large market for steel pipe gave way to a relatively small market for polyethylene pipe. Polyethylene pipe is not only durable but it is so light and easy to move that it can be taken out and reused when a shaft is abandoned.

The flexibility of polyethylene pipe is one of its greatest advantages, because it permits it to be coiled and shipped in long lengths which can be laid directly without the cost or trouble of couplings. While standard lengths are only 200 to 400 feet, there have been special cases where reels of pipe as long as one mile have been made and transported to the site on special trailers. The saving in time and labor in such a case makes the polyethylene pipe installation much cheaper than its equivalent in steel, even where the steel pipe price per foot is lower.

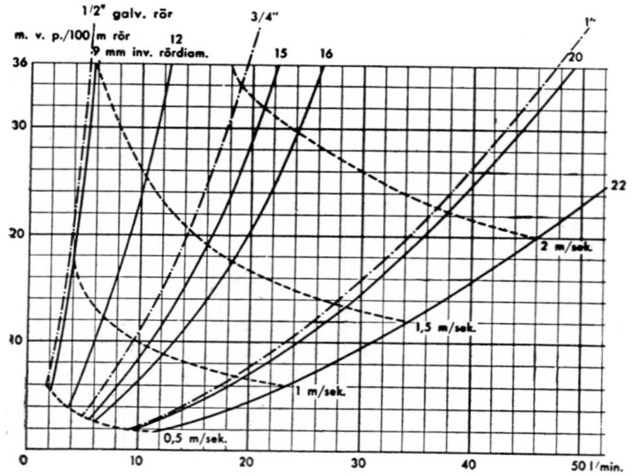

Figure 7–1. Water flow through polyethylene and galvanized iron pipe.
———, polyethylene pipe, diameter millimeters.
. — . —, galvanized pipe, diameter in inches.
(*Courtesy Svenska Metalverke*)

An important consideration in the use of polyethylene pipe is the fact that an appreciable reduction in pipe diameter is possible, compared to galvanized steel pipe. Figure 7-1 is taken from some Swedish work and while galvanized pipe diameters have been converted into inches other data have been left in metric units since their only purpose here is to show the comparison between steel and polyethylene. The pressure along the left-side of the graph is given in meters of water head per 100 meters of pipe and the flow across the bottom is given in liters per minute. The dashed lines are for galvanized steel pipe and solid lines for polyethylene. A polyethylene pipe size can be chosen which gives slightly more flow than the galvanized steel pipe. It will be seen that polyethylene pipe always has a smaller diameter; as a matter of fact, it is almost a pipe size smaller.

The fact that corrosion and build-up of lime deposits will reduce the flow in the galvanized pipe quite rapidly, whereas polyethylene pipe will retain its full capacity indefinitely is often of greater significance than the initial flow data.

Polyethylene pipe is joined to fittings and to other piping in a variety of ways. The commonest method in the United States is the insert type fitting used with an external strap clamp. The insert is usually a molded high-impact styrene piece and the strap clamp is of stainless steel. There are numerous disadvantages to this system: the flow diameter is quite severely restricted at the fitting; the chemical resistance of the styrene is appreciably poorer than that of the polyethylene; the stainless steel clamp is relatively expensive. In spite of these weaknesses it is still widely used, mainly because it is so simple to install. As long as polyethylene pipe is installed by amateurs, or by plumbers used to working with metal, it is important to have a method of joining that requires no special tools or skill.

Large installations, installed by specialists in polyethylene pipe, are usually welded, since they generally require the greatest chemical resistance, or are calculated most closely as to their carrying capacities.

Polyethylene pipe can be welded by the hot-gas technique using a polyethylene welding rod and a special hot gas torch. This technique is described in detail in Chapter 5. It requires considerable skill and can only be used by trained welders.

Upset butt welding is also practicable and has been developed to a high degree in Europe. The tube must be cut absolutely perpendicular, after which the ends are chamfered 30° inward.

The tube ends are heated by holding them close to a radiating source of heat, e.g., an electric radiator (Figure 7-2) or a tin with plane-parallel sides which is heated inside by a gas flame or a blow torch. When the ends of the pipe are melted the source of heat is removed and the ends are quickly brought together and lightly pressed against one another while being slowly revolved. The tubes must be accurately centered and pressed together with the proper pressure so that the chamfer is completely filled without too much flash forming inside the tube. This method also requires great skill and experience.

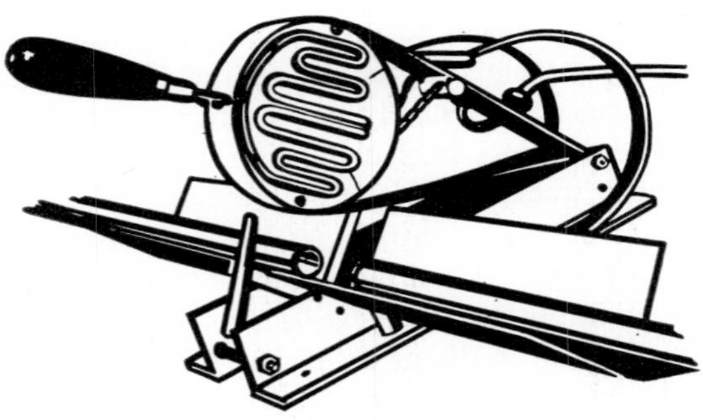

Figure 7–2. Apparatus for heating ends of pipe for butt welding. (*Courtesy Svenska Metalverke*)

The flange joint is especially adapted to industrial applications where it may be necessary to disassemble the installation from time to time. One of the best types of flange joints is made by forming the rings against which the flanges press out of the end of the pipe. A special tool is used to form the rings (Figure 7-3).

The procedure is as follows:

(1) The loose flanges are placed on the tube. Their holes should be about $\frac{1}{16}$ inch larger than the diameter of the tube and the sides of the holes should be rounded where they meet the flange.

(2) The drift (1) is pushed into the tube up to the mark on the drift.

(3) The tube is gripped in the vise (2). The end of the tube must project from the jaws of the vise sufficiently far for the tube material to be formed into a flange.

(4) The polyethylene pipe is now carefully heated with a flame until it is "soaked" and in melting condition.

(5) The shaping tool (3) is inserted so that it engages with the drift (1) after which the screw (4) is quickly tightened (see B and C, Figure 7-3).

(6) The polyethylene pipe and the tools are now left to cool.

(7) The shaping tool (3) is removed.

(8) The drift (1) is withdrawn by passing the coupling (5) over drift (1) and screw (4), after which the drift can be drawn out with the screw (see D, Figure 7-3).

(9) The vise (2) is released and the tool is removed.

(10) Any burrs on the flange can be easily removed with a sharp knife, after which the flange is ready for assembly.

Because of the comparative softness of polyethylene pipe no packing is required between the flange surfaces, nor should they have sealing paste applied to them. The flange joint must, of course, be uniformly tight, but not so tight as a flange joint in steel or copper tubes.

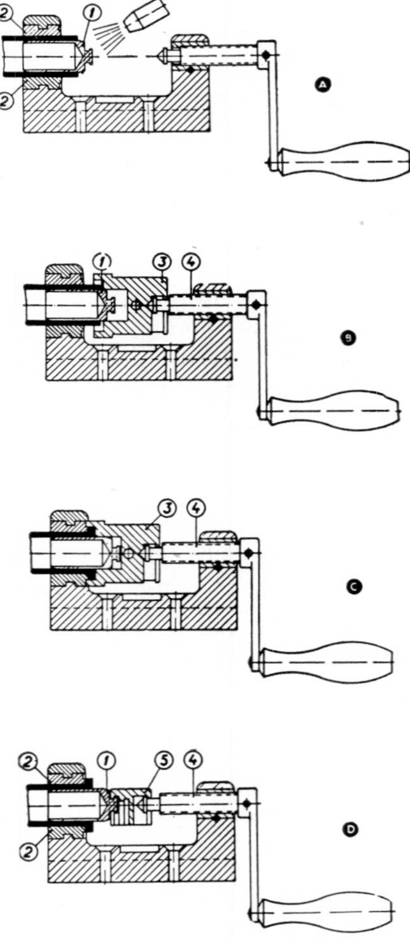

Figure 7–3. Method of making integral flanges on polyethylene pipe. (*Courtesy Svenska Metalverke*)

It is possible to join polyethylene pipe by means of regular threaded pipe fittings if certain precautions are observed. In the first place, only pipe designed for this purpose should be used as many polyethylene pipes do not have enough of a wall thickness to thread. Adjustable pipe dies should be used which can be adjusted to give a tighter fit than with steel pipe. Before thread cutting starts a steel tube or wooden dowel of suitable dimensions must be placed in the polyethylene pipe as it is not practical to thread polyethylene pipe without internal support. During cutting the polyethylene pipe should be held in a special vise with wooden faces to prevent damage. The pipe die should be very sharp. There is very little wear as a result of cutting polyethylene so the dies have a long life. The cut should not be oblique as this causes eccentric thinning of the wall. Oil should never be used under any circumstances, and if the die has been previously oiled it must be washed in gasoline.

When the joint is assembled a metal insert should be placed in the end of the pipe. If this is not inserted the joint will creep under pressure. Care must be taken not to cross threads when inserting the pipe into a fitting since the polyethylene is so soft that the fitting will readily cut across the thread causing the joint to leak. A good joint can generally be made with hand tightening. A wrench should never be used; if necessary, wooden tongs can be used to tighten it.

Metal couplings similar to those used with copper tubing can also be used, but these should have a serrated inner cone as shown in Figure 7-4. The end of the tube should be heated so it will expand over the cone. Couplings of this general design, molded of rigid PVC are also available.

Since polyethylene pipe expands a great deal more when heated than steel pipe, provision must be made for expansion. This can be done with conventional expansion bends on exposed installations; buried lines should be laid into the trench with slight bends rather than absolutely straight lines.

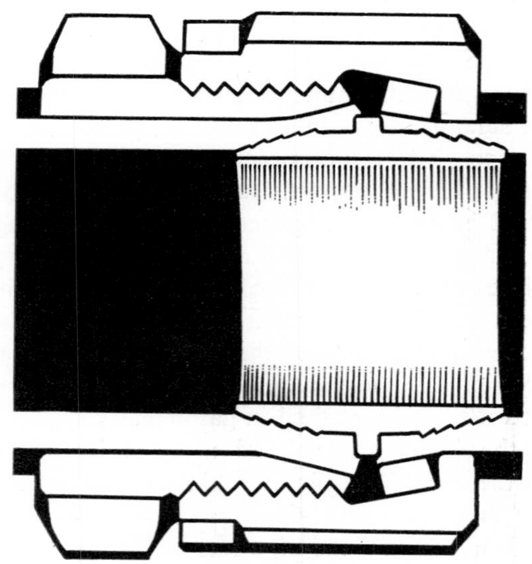

Figure 7–4. Screw coupling for polyethylene pipe. (*Courtesy Svenska Metalverke*)

Perhaps the ultimate way to get long, continuous lengths of polyethylene pipe is by an extruder, mounted on a truck, which is capable of making and laying pipe continuously. This evidently gets around any limitation whatsoever on the length of pipe that can be laid.

While urban installations of polyethylene pipe for drinking water are increasing rapidly, the inherent conservatism of the central water authorities has limited its use. Its really large use has been in rural water supplies where there is no mass of regulations to contend with, and where the farmer can, in general, do his own installation. Figure 7-5 shows the ease with which polyethylene pipe can be handled.

Figure 7–5. Long lengths of polyethylene pipe can be easily carried. (*Courtesy Spencer Chemical Co.*)

An interesting development along this line has been the use of double pipes in jet-well installation. The jet-well pump provides a means of using an inexpensive and reliable centrifugal pump on wells too deep for the limited lift of these pumps. Ordinary deep-well pumps have the entire pump mechanism at the bottom of the well. This is expensive and makes any repair a major operation. In the jet well there is only a venturi tube at the bottom of the well. The pump forces water under pressure down a pipe into the well and through the venturi. The venturi tube picks up additional water at the bottom of the well and the larger amount of water rises out of the well. A portion of the flow is constantly recirculated and the remainder drawn off for use. This operation requires two pipes when metal is used. Special polyethylene pipe is made for this purpose consisting of two joined pipes of appropriate sizes. This greatly facilitates installation because the two pipes handle like one. Also, since the polyethylene is flexible, a continuous length can be used for any well depth and it can be inserted into, or removed from the well without using a derrick or rigging. Since many ground waters corrode metal, polyethylene pipe often lasts longer, and the chance for a metallic taste to develop is reduced.

In many cases, the availability of polyethylene pipe makes it economically feasible to install a farm water system where it could not be done with any other pipe. It is estimated that considering material and installation costs, a farm water system can be installed using polyethylene pipe for about one-third less than with any other pipe.

Another application that uses a great deal of polyethylene pipe is the lawn sprinkler kit. Here, again, the primary advantage is the ease with which the householder can assemble his own installation without any special tools or equipment. Kits generally contain polyethylene pipe, brass or plastic sprinkler heads, tees, clamps, nipples, ells and adapters. The only tools needed are a knife or hacksaw to cut the pipe, pliers and a screwdriver to fasten the clamps, a spade to dig a trench, and a pipe wrench to make the connection to the water supply if metal is being used. Figure 7-6 shows such a kit.

In order to assure complete coverage with the available water pressure the locations of the sprinkler heads should be laid out on a scale drawing of the lawn. The pipe is then cut to the lengths indicated, and joined to the sprinkler heads with the fittings and clamps supplied. The assembly is laid out over the area, as indicated by the scale drawing, and a stake is driven in the ground near each sprinkler head. The sprinkler heads are then tied or taped to the stakes vertically and the connection is made to the water service. The system is tested by turning on the water, and the location of the sprinklers can be changed to get the best possible coverage. The ground is then thoroughly soaked to soften it, and a trench of the proper depth is cut in the lawn under each pipe, burying it so that the sprinkler heads are exactly flush with the surface.

Figure 7–6. Complete kit for installation of underground sprinkler system using polyethylene pipe. (*Courtesy Spencer Chemical Co.*)

While it is possible to accomplish the same thing with other types of pipe, it is by no means as easy. The flexibility of polyethylene pipe enables it to follow the ground contours and its elasticity makes it resistant to frost damage so that it is unnecessary to make any provision for draining the system in the winter. The "do-it-yourself feature," however, is what really sells it.

An objection that has been raised to polyethylene pipe is that it is eaten by rodents. An investigation was recently made of polyethylene pipe that had been in service for some time. Rumors of rodent problems were common but in no case could an actual instance be verified or a sample of gnawed pipe be found.

As a further check, starved rats were barred from food by a series of copper, lead, vinyl and polyethylene pipes. The rats concentrated on gnawing the lead and vinyl pipes, practically ignoring the copper and polyethylene. These tests proved the rodent problem is more a matter of rumor than of fact.

Applications of Polyethylene in Wire and Cable

As mentioned earlier, the first use of polyethylene was for telephone cable insulation. This led to a whole series of uses, mostly of a military nature, which kept polyethylene on allocation for years. Coaxial cable for radio frequency use is now generally insulated with polyethylene. Interesting developments have been made to improve the characteristics of high-frequency cable, some of which involve the use of polyethylene. Figure 7-7 shows an air-dielectric cable using a polyethylene filament to center the conductor.

Figure 7–7. High frequency cable using polyethylene filament to center inner conductor.
(*Courtesy Phelps Dodge Copper Products Corp.*)

Outstanding properties and advantages of this cable include the following:

(1) Long continuous lengths on reels
(2) Excellent uniformity
(3) Low attenuation
(4) Permanent electrical properties
(5) No radiation
(6) Light weight and high strength
(7) Flexibility at low temperatures.

Community antenna TV systems require a coaxial network cable having broad band response together with minimum attenuation. The television signal must be transmitted from a remote antenna to a distant service area. A transmission line of 10 to 20 miles is not unusual.

Low attenuation enables the system operator to transmit these signals greater distances per amplifier. As a consequence, the number of amplifiers along the antenna run can be reduced, thereby decreasing both the operator's maintenance costs and the amount of noise introduced into the circuit.

Permanence of electrical characteristics is most important. Replacement of conventional RG-type cable, due to deterioration of electrical characteristics with age, has in many instances created an additional operational expense.

The occurrence of radiation throughout these TV networks is a very real problem. Its importance is attested by recent studies made by industry committees to determine the practical aspects of the problem, such as main sources of radiation, maximum permissible radiation levels, and suitable methods of control. These advantages are rapidly increasing the demand for this type of cable.

Another improved polyethylene insulated coaxial design uses foamed polyethylene as dielectric. This was originally developed for the aircraft industry which desired lower attenuation, lighter weight, and better permanence of properties. The filament type of cable was considered undesirable because these cables had to be pressurized for use at high altitudes.

For aircraft applications, it is obvious that cable weight must be a primary consideration. For this reason, a copper tube inner conductor was incorporated in the design. An aluminum sheath improves the cable efficiency without an increase in weight as compared to the more conventional braid and jacket constructions. In addition, the sheath provides an excellent protective covering, guarding against external contamination.

Foamed polyethylene offers a practical form of homogeneous air-filled dielectric, which can be expected to retain its normal dielectric strength at high altitudes without pressurization. Furthermore, the reduction of dielectric constant, compared to solid polyethylene, assured a lower attenuation up to about 1000 megacycles.

Aside from the special applications in the aircraft industry, foamed polyethylene cable appears to be an excellent low-loss, air-dielectric cable for general use. Attenuation-wise, it is better than solid dielectric cables covered with either copper braid or aluminum tube. It appears to exhibit improved uniformity compared to braided type cables. Because of the additional protection offered by the aluminum sheath, the properties of foamed polyethylene cable should not deteriorate with age or environmental conditions. Foamed polyethylene cable offers the designer a low-loss uniform semi-flexible cable that can be expected to retain its properties throughout its service life.

One of the largest-volume uses of polyethylene coated wire was for army field wire. Its construction is extremely interesting because it requires light weight and durability as well as insulating characteristics. This was accomplished by extruding a thin nylon coating over the polyethylene insulation to give it the abrasion resistance lacking in polyethylene.

Among civilian applications, the Atlantic telephone cable uses a huge amount of polyethylene which serves not only as primary insulation on the conductor, but also as a waterproof sheathing outside the steel armor cables. Additional armor wire is used in shallower waters. One of the most remarkable features of this cable is that throughout its length there are periodically large "pods," also polyethylene sheathed, which carry repeaters to increase the volume of the message. The sheathing is of high molecular weight polyethylene, compounded with polyisobutylene, antioxidant and carbon black. Its life is estimated in excess of twenty years.

Less spectacular, but perhaps more important in improved telephone communication, is a polyethylene insulated telephone cable and distribution wire. A few years ago the Michigan Bell Telephone Company pointed out their urgent need for a low cost multi-pair wire facility for use in sparsely populated areas. In order to extend service in these areas, long distances must be traversed with a small group of circuits. The facility had to be suitable for installation on existing pole lines which already carried so many open wire circuits that it was extremely difficult or impossible to add open wire pairs without extensively rebuilding the line. Long spans would frequently be encountered. Above all, the installation cost of the facility had to be low.

B Rural Wire was developed to fulfill these requirements, consisting of six twisted pairs of insulated annealed copper No. 19 AWG (0.036-inch diameter) conductors cabled around an insulated .109 inch extra high-strength steel support wire. Each conductor is insulated with polyethylene, with an outer covering of polyvinyl chloride to provide added toughness during installation and color coding for ring, tip and pair identification. Originally, the rural wire was made with a black PVC compound because the colored compounds

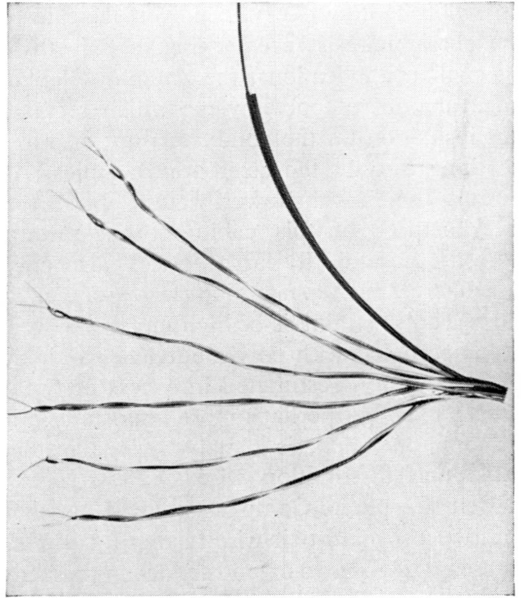

Figure 7–8. Colored B Rural Wire.
(*Courtesy Wire & Wire Products*)

available at that time did not have satisfactory weathering properties. When colored compounds satisfactory for outdoor use were developed, the jackets on B Rural Wire were changed. The insulated conductors are twisted into pairs of different twist length to keep down cross-talk. The support wire is insulated with polyethylene which provides adequate electrical breakdown strength between conductors and the steel wire. Figure 7-8 shows the color coded rural wire, the black wire being mated in turn with blue, red, green, brown, slate, and yellow.

The advantage which this wire possesses compared to the conventional type of small cables are headed by the fact that it is self-supporting. Because of its sheathless construction, splicing and terminating are simple operations requiring no costly or elaborate sealing techniques. From a transmission standpoint, the primary concern is the change in its characteristics between dry and wet weather conditions. In general, moisture increases capacitance, conductance, and attenuation, and decreases impedance, cutoff frequency of loaded wire, capacitance unbalance, and carrier frequency cross-talk. These present some problems in the wide-spread use of the wire. However, the B Rural Wire may be used in ordinary subscriber loops pretty much as though it were regular sheathed 19-gauge cable, including the use of H88 loading. It can be used for distances of about 10 miles, except where a signalling limit may further restrict the usable length of the B Rural Wire. Ease of installation was one of the main features of this wire. Figure 7-9 shows extremely quick and simple the way it is attached to the pole.

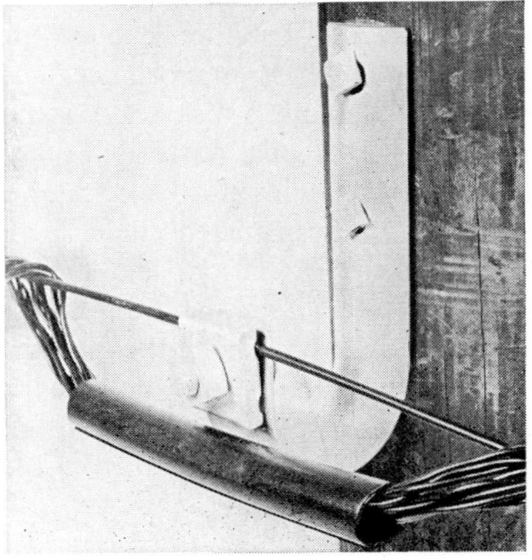

Figure 7–9. Method of attaching B Rural Wire to a pole using a bracket. (*Courtesy Wire & Wire Products*)

The need for this type of wire was shown by its rapid acceptance. Over 40,000,000 linear feet of B Rural Wire were used in 1954, its first year in the Bell System, and its use has grown rapidly since.

Figure 7–10. Telephone cable insulated and sheathed with polyethylene. (*Courtesy Bell Telephone Co.*)

In addition to its use in high-frequency cable and rural distribution cable, polyethylene plays an important role in communication wire—multiconduction cable for long distance transmission or for area distribution cables. In these cables the low power factor is of less importance, and in a larger cable the saving in eliminating the jacket is not important. The primary advantage of polyethylene insulation is that a break in the cable jacket does not cause immediate service failure as it does in paper insulated cable. Water inside the jacket does not hurt the insulation, and the need for completely waterproofing the joints and terminals is eliminated. Figure 7-10 shows an experimental cable that has given good service. The conductors are polyethylene insulated and the cable is sheathed with a composite aluminum and polyethylene structure. The use of such cables is rapidly increasing.

The application of polyethylene to wire used for the transmission of electric power has had a less rapid development partly due to the fact that power cables generally operate at relatively high temperatures which soften the polyethylene excessively. Another weakness is that, when operated at high voltages, the slightest bubble or gap between conductor and plastic causes the development of corona which quickly destroys the insulation. For operation at relatively low voltage and power, as for instance in street lighting wire or in house wiring, it has been quite successful. One objection to the use of polyethylene insulation in home wiring is the relative flammability of the product. This can be overcome by proper compounding, and polyethylene compounds are now available that are no more flammable than any other insulating material.

Miscellaneous Small Extrusions

There are also numerous small uses for polyethylene extrusion such as tubing for blood plasma and blood transfusion, where it eliminates the risk of contamination by plasticizers used with vinyls. It is also widely used for small catheter tubes where its slightly increased stiffness and improved chemical resistance are advantages over most vinyl compounds.

Polyethylene belts are commonly used on inexpensive dresses. Solid extruded polyethylene makes an attractive belt that is considerably more durable than the vinyl coated or resin coated fabrics.

The use of extruded polyethylene welting is increasing constantly both in the shoe and furniture trade as a result of the good service experienced with it. The absence of a plasticizer, which attacks wood finishes, or is lost, with consequent shrinkage and embrittlement is the main advantage here.

The use of polyethylene extruded gaskets is also increasing. The excellent low-temperature flexibility of polyethylene makes it particularly valuable for refrigeration and freezer uses. Polyethylene drinking straws have become quite popular in the homes as they are reusable. Figure 7-11 shows some straws made by a special multi-color extrusion technique.

Figure 7–11. Multi-colored polyethylene tubes for use as sipper straws (*Courtesy E. I. duPont de Nemours & Co.*)

The polyethylene tower packing shown in Figure 7-12 is especially valuable for use with corrosive materials, or materials that must be protected from contamination. The lightweight of this packing reduces the weight of tower construction necessary and thus reduces costs. The shape of the packing assures maximum contact efficiency with the least possible resistance to flow.

Polyethylene components have been used to improve many things in recent years. One of these is the storage battery, in which slotted polyethylene tubes are used to hold the positive plate material (Figure 7-13). This not only increases the

Figure 7–12. Polyethylene tower packing.
(*Courtesy Harshaw Chemical Co.*)

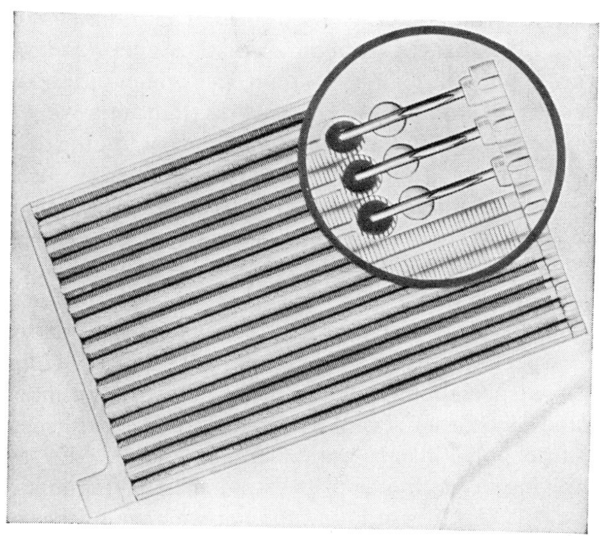

Figure 7–13. Polyethylene slotted tube battery plate.
(*Courtesy Electric Storage Battery Co.*)

effective plate area as compared to a flat plate, but also holds the plate material more firmly, thus increasing the life of the battery. Polyethylene is so resistant to battery acid that no deterioration occurs during the life of the battery.

Polyethylene Monofilament

The present applications of polyethylene monofilament depend largely on the special properties described in Chapter 2.

The U. S. Coastguard uses a certain amount of polyethylene monofilament cordage for life-saving work because it will not absorb water and sink. It also retains its clean, bright color which improves visibility.

Polyethylene monofilament is used for two specialized types of filter cloths. One is used for the filtration of corrosive solutions, where its chemical inertness is particularly valuable, and the other is used for air filtration. When a stream of air is passed through a polyethylene monofilament cloth an electrical charge is built up which attracts dust particles to the filament. This means that relatively open meshes can be used and still remove most of the dust. A variety of special fabrics are available for this purpose.

Polyethylene monofilament can also be used for insect screens and for automobile seat covers. Pigmented materials are generally used for these to protect the polyethylene from the action of sunlight.

An interesting application has recently been developed to make a special fabric for automobile seats. The fabric is woven in a special construction using polyethylene monofilament and another fiber. After weaving, a heat treatment shrinks the polyethylene monofilament and buckles up the fabric giving a permanent three-dimensional configuration which makes it self-ventilating for hot weather driving.

8. APPLICATIONS OF POLYETHYLENE MOLDINGS, BLOWN BOTTLES, VACUUM FORMINGS, AND PIECES MADE BY MISCELLANEOUS PROCESSES

While the largest volume uses of polyethylene have already been discussed, some of the most varied and interesting applications will be covered in this chapter. A few technical matters will be discussed where the substitution of polyethylene for other materials has raised special problems.

The injection molding technique is tremendously versatile, and has been developed to a point where a solid piece of almost any conceivable shape can be made. The basic position of polyethylene in the injection molding field differs greatly from that in the film and pipe field. In most injection molding applications polyethylene is more expensive than competitive materials. Not only is the price higher, but because of its flexibility it is often necessary to make the walls heavier, thus using more polyethylene than would be needed with a competitive plastic. The rapid growth of polyethylene in injection molding, especially for housewares, is based entirely on the superior properties of the resulting products. The key to its success in housewares is unbreakability. It is frequently called "the unbreakable plastic," and in fact many articles made from it are for all practical purposes unbreakable. The technical basis for this has been discussed in Chapter 2.

The recent success of polyethylene in large and relatively expensive household items has in part been made possible because some smaller article has given excellent service. For many years plastics had a reputation of being cheap and breakable making it impossible to use them in an article that represented any considerable investment. Polyethylene has broken down this barrier and it is presently possible to merchandise articles of any practicable size. Its growth into large and relatively expensive items has been spectacular. It is important because it penetrates fields entirely new to plastics, replacing metals and wood. It may only be the start in a trend that could see almost any household article made of polyethylene.

One of the first items to obtain wide acceptance was the "juice shaker." The appearance of frozen orange juice had created a demand for a means of mixing it adequately. Various attempts in glass, metal and polystyrene had produced rather unsatisfactory results. The resilience of polyethylene permitted the development of a tongue-and-groove-type closure that made it practicable to put a cover on a wide mouth jar and still have it completely waterproof. The addition of a pouring spout to this assembly made it the first really satisfactory juice shaker which soon became a necessity in every household. The early cylindrical ones were superceded by rectangular and various other shapes. Polyethylene drinking "glasses" were a natural to go with the shaker.

The polyethylene mixing bowl, unbreakable, quiet, and incapable of bending an eggbeater soon became available in all standard sizes. Some of these were made with a thin rim which could be shaped by hand to make a pour spout, and others had a rigid rim. The smaller sizes were used as cereal dishes for children and a special tip-proof version in various sizes was used for dog and cat dishes.

The flexibility and good release properties of polyethylene made it popular for gelatin molds, some of which are made in the traditional fluted shapes, designed by Egyptian coppersmiths at the very dawn of civilization.

Formidable technical problems had to be solved before polyethylene could be used for the larger items, but by now a whole new size range was possible. Large, flat pieces such as drainboards became possible and these were followed by dish-pans, baby baths, wastebaskets, and garbage pails. The light weight, unbreakability and noise reducing nature of these pieces assured their popularity. Figure 8-1 shows a trash can molded of polyethylene.

Figure 8–1. 22-gallon trash can molded of polyethylene. (*Courtesy Spencer Chemical Co.*)

The refrigerator was the focal point of many applications. The excellent low-temperature properties and moisture resistance of polyethylene recommended it for a variety of refrigerator dishes, ice-cube trays, refrigerator water jars, etc.

The growth of the home freezer developed a whole series of covered containers. Unlike the polyethylene bag which was used as an expendable item, these molded freezer jars can be reused year after year, their relatively high initial cost being justified by their long life.

While traditional materials are still fighting a rear-guard action, the conquest of the housewares field by polyethylene is almost an accomplished fact, except in cooking pans and in some accessories where stiffness is still essential.

Polyethylene sand toys in traditional and novel shapes have largely replaced the rather dangerous stamped metal toys. Many toy airplanes are now made of polyethylene and some inroads have been made into the model car field. Ingenious novelty items appear every day using polyethylene. A helicopter with a rotor which spins high into the air, for instance, is usable indoors only because the flexible polyethylene rotor does no damage to house furnishings.

The doll field is represented by many small solid figures which may or may not be jointed. There are replacements for the tin soldier. It appears however, that there is considerable room for further development of polyethylene in this field.

The field of injection molded components for electrical and mechanical assemblies really demonstrates the versatility of polyethylene. To date, these have not attained the size found in housewares moldings, but they make up for this in complexity and strict tolerance requirements. Typical of these is a parts holder for a proximity fuse that has been molded by many firms. It is a roughly cylindrical object about

1½ inches in diameter and 1¼ inches high, with 32 small holes ranging in diameter from ¼ to under 1/16 inch. Some of these change in diameter, but all of them have to be held to very close tolerances.

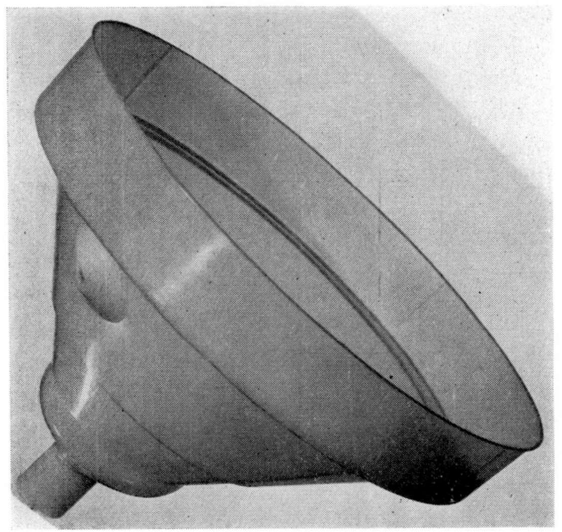

Figure 8–2. Television tube shield made of polyethylene. (*Courtesy Eastman Chemical Products, Inc.*)

Probably the largest electronic component made of polyethylene is the television color picture tube shield. As shown in Figure 8-2, this is a complete envelope for the entire picture tube, except for the face. It protects the tube from accumulation of static on the outside and from dust. On the other end of the scale are tiny and delicate capacitors and resistors which have injection molded jackets to protect them from moisture and mechanical shock. Molding the jackets for these components requires extreme care to prevent damage to the piece. Polyethylene is also used for numerous small insulators in electronic assemblies.

Another use, not connected with electronics, is for electric fence insulators. The resilience of the polyethylene makes the application possible in this case as the insulators are molded in such a way that the wire is merely snapped into place where it is held tightly. A really remarkable molding in polyethylene is called a rocket fuse wire spacer. A polyethylene disc about 3½ inches in diameter and only .015 inch thick is molded around a wire. Its purpose is to hold the wire in place under any handling conditions, seal the rocket against moisture, and then to be consumed almost instantaneously when the rocket fires.

Polyethylene moldings are widely used as closures. Perhaps the largest item of polyethylene injection molding, is the collapsible tube cap. The inertness and resilience of polyethylene makes any sort of gasket or washer unnecessary. The cap seals tightly, yet never sticks. The low specific gravity of polyethylene, and the short molding cycle, usually on completely automatic machines, make these caps cheaper than any suitable alternative.

Aerosol "bomb" valves and detergent can spouts are examples of other special-purpose closures made successfully of polyethylene.

Polyethylene droppers have almost replaced glass for the pharmaceutical industry. The impossibility of breakage and the decreased danger of damaging the eyes are largely responsible for their success. In some cases, polyethylene has replaced rubber as well. For instance, where the dropper will be used for some time, the polyethylene deteriorates less rapidly and has better resistance to many medical ingredients. The polyethylene bulb also is less likely to contaminate material that might be drawn up into it. If the dropper is to

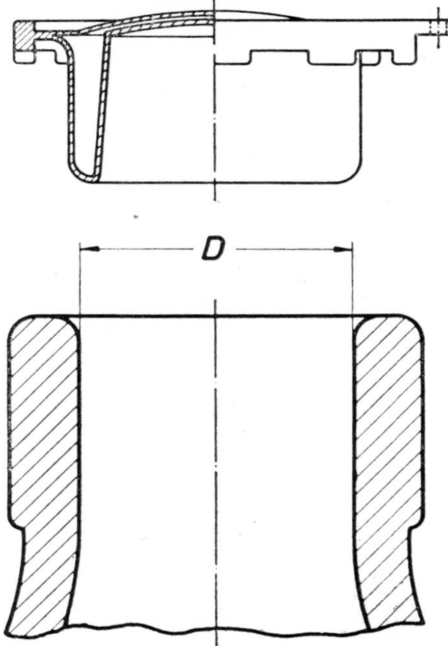

Figure 8–3. Polyethylene bottle cap.
(*Courtesy Golde Co.*)

be used in a screw-cap closure, the entire assembly can be made of polyethylene. The cap and bulb can be molded in one piece, and the dropper held in by a snap fit. The squeeze bottle spray nozzle is another widely used closure, resilience and chemical inertness being the reasons.

There are, however, many types of closures that were especially designed for polyethylene and which make particular use of its unique properties. Typical of these is a series of grooved caps made in Germany for anything from a bottle to a large dairy can, the general design of which is shown in Figure 8-3. They are widely used in the chemical, pharmaceutical and foodstuff industries.

The ease of molding small parts in polyethylene has led to its development in many applications related to closures such as capliners, plugs, orifice reducers, applicators and essential parts of many atomizers, dispensers, lotion pumps, etc.

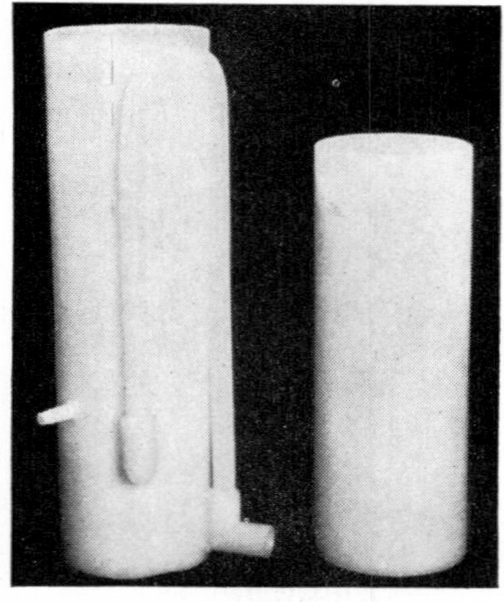

Figure 8–4. Pipet washer made entirely of polyethylene. (*Courtesy Bel-Art Products*)

A considerable number of polyethylene moldings are made in the form of laboratory glassware, funnels, beakers (see Figure 8-4) graduates, for example. In addition to being unbreakable, these pieces are resistant to many chemicals which attack glass, such as hydrofluoric acid. They are also useful where contamination of the contents with silica or other glass components must be avoided. The disadvantage of low-heat resistance can be partially overcome by radiation, and a considerable amount of irradiated polyethylene laboratory equipment has been made, especially for use by the Atomic Energy Commission.

Figure 8–5. Soil pipe joint cover.
(*Courtesy Boco Industries*)

Injection molded parts for almost any purpose appear daily. Figure 8-5 shows an ingenious application. A joint cover has been designed of polyethylene to replace the conventional tar-paper wrapping used around field tiles to combat the problem of keeping soil and stones from sewage disposal systems. The clip is 2½ inches wide and long enough to cover the top and sides of the tiles. The bottom remains open for dispersal or collection of liquids. The new clip also simplifies installation; a fin molded into the top serves as a handle for snapping the tile clip in place and also as a guide for proper alignment. A lug molded on the inside of the clip indicates proper spacing for the tiles.

Figure 8–6. Polyethylene top for paint cans.
(*Courtesy No Mus Products, Inc.*)

The messy job usually associated with household painting chores when an open can of paint is being used can be largely eliminated by fitting a molded polyethylene collar-shaped top over the rim of the can. (Figure 8-6) Resistant to the chemicals found in most paints, the tough, flexible top is easy to install—and just as easy to remove. An undercut groove molded into the rim of the polyethylene guard simply snaps over the bead on the top of the can. Once in place, the collar keeps the rim of the can completely free from paint, allows extra stirring space, keeps the paint from splashing out, serves as a good pouring spout, and it is designed with a straight-edged lip for wiping excess paint from the brush.

An optional accessory to the automobile storage battery, which proved so popular as to influence the design of batteries was the automatic watering cell. This consists of a small polyethylene bottle so arranged as to replace the cap on the battery cell. When filled it automatically allows the water to flow into the cell as required. The polyethylene is transparent enough to show the water level at a glance, thus eliminating the need to open the battery for inspection, and with the relatively large water reserve it is not necessary to add water as often. Its popularity has resulted in batteries being made with larger water reserves to reduce the amount of checking required. The all-polyethylene battery case is technically practical but so far the cost has limited its use.

A widely used, but rarely seen application is for molded shoe parts. The first shoe part to be molded of polyethylene was the counter—the part that holds the heel in shape.

Polyethylene had a tremendous vogue in the jewelry business with the poppet bead. These beads, with a hole in one side and a short stem with a little ball on the other side, require no string, but are assembled by popping the ball of one bead into the hole of another where it can rotate freely, but is still held firmly. A woman can assemble them in any way she desires—bracelets, chokers, long strands, changing them as often as she likes. The wide possibilities in colors and shapes have kept them in vogue for a long time. Earrings and "pearls" for a wide variety of jewelry, millinery and dressmaking uses are also molded from polyethylene.

The resilience of polyethylene makes it possible to mold a box and cover with an integral hinge, the hinge being merely a thin section in the molding. A sewing machine accessory kit of this type has been made for some time. Cosmetic cases, lunch boxes, instrument boxes and a wide variety of small and medium sized cases are made in this manner.

One of the most extraordinary kinds of moldings made of polyethylene is that which simulates lace, filigree work, or pierced ivory carvings. Doilies, place mats, coasters, lamp shades, bottle or glass holders, etc., can be made, closely simulating the fine detail of the most delicate designs. Because of the toughness and resilience of polyethylene, even the most delicate traceries are quite durable.

Blown Bottles

The public associates polyethylene with the "squeeze bottle" more than with any other article. The idea of blowing a plastic bottle by a modification of the glass-bottle techniques was conceived before polyethylene was ever known. Acetate bottles were blown in the thirties by the Plax Corporation. The advantages of these compared to glass containers, however, did not justify their added cost. They were unbreakable, but rather readily attacked by many materials and served no purpose other than that of a container. The squeeze bottle, on the other hand, serves both as a container and as a dispenser, a dual function which in many cases justifies its extra cost.

The polyethylene blown bottle, by no means limited to the dispensing of toilet preparations, has found wide markets where an unbreakable bottle, especially resistant to chemical attack, is needed. Its obvious replacement of the soft wax bottle used for hydrofluoric acid soon led to its use for acid and chemical bottles ranging from small sizes up to 15-gallon carboys. The lightness and unbreakability of these bottles greatly simplified the shipment of chemicals, requiring no crating or special handling.

A number of shipping containers for chemicals are coming into use. Although they are not all made by the bottle-blowing technique they are being grouped together here because they have a similar function. Shown in Figure 8-7 are plywood-jacketed, blow-molded polyethylene carboys, available in 6½ and 13 gallon capacities. Square carboys are molded in two pieces, joined by heat sealing, and bolted together with steel edging. Encased in thick wood boxes and used with a tip stand they are particularly adapted to plant dispensing. Both of these containers have full approval of the ICC, under recommendations of the Bureau of Explosives.

Figure 8–7. Polyethylene carboys in plywood containers. (*Courtesy General Chemical Div., Allied Chemical & Dye Corp.*)

In addition to its use as a general shipping container, the polyethylene bottle also serves as a liner for corrugated board boxes. Special bottles which fit into a corrugated box make a remarkably light and inexpensive shipping container for all types of liquids. The liners are flexible enough to stack into each other to save space when shipped empty.

The bottle-blowing technique is extremely versatile. Where cost is a major factor, the wall of the bottle can be blown as thin as .005 inch, permitting it to be used as a disposable container. The introduction of the dry-charged automobile battery has created a demand for an inexpensive, unbreakable, acid-resistant container for the sulfuric acid that has to be shipped with each battery. Polyethylene is particularly adaptable to this use and a number of containers have been made for this purpose. One, a thin-walled blown polyethylene bottle, placed in a suitable cardboard case, is extremely satisfactory. The others, while not strictly bottles, will be mentioned here to avoid redundancy. They are a heavy-walled polyethylene bag, and bottles made of two vacuum-formed halves, heat-sealed together. These are heat-sealed after filling to be sure there is no leakage, and have some kind of pour spout, the end of which is snipped off when the acid is poured into the battery. Generally, each battery is accompanied by a bottle containing the exact amount of acid for each cell.

Figure 8-8 shows one of a wide variety of special-purpose bottles made of polyethylene.

One of the problems that arises is that the automatic handling equipment developed for use with glass bottles will not handle the polyethylene bottles, mainly because of their light weight. This not only prevents satisfactory operation of devices like unscramblers which line bottles up on a conveyor belt, but the empty bottles will not even stand up by themselves on a moving belt. To overcome this, each bottle is hand-placed into a polyethylene cup of the exact size to hold the bottle and fastened to a moving belt which carries the bottle through the entire filling operation. Evidently this means that whenever the bottle size is changed the entire set of cups has to be changed. However, it is worth the effort because by means of these cups standard automatic filling machines can be used for the squeeze bottles.

Figure 8–8. One of the many types of polyethylene bottles available today. (*Courtesy Plax Corp.*)

Every squeeze bottle with a spray is equipped with a plug and capillary tube also made of polyethylene. The plug and tube are assembled in automatic or semi-automatic machines, and the assembly is dropped into the filled bottle by hand. Final seating of the plug in the bottle neck is done by a machine, and the closure is applied automatically, making filling rapid and inexpensive.

Heavy-duty rectangular "bottles" have also been developed which permit much more efficient use of space when shipping liquids in small containers.

Closely related in many uses to the polyethylene bottle but made in an entirely different way is the Bracon container. Only one firm makes these in the United States. The process originated in Switzerland. Its first version was as a collapsible tube to replace soft metal. It is made by extruding a thin polyethylene tube for the main body of the container and then molding a shoulder and means of closure onto one end of it. During this process, the tube is on a metal mandrel and can be printed while it is supported on this. Much better printing is possible than on a blown bottle supported only by air or liquid pressure inside. For use as a collapsible tube, a closure is applied, and it is filled through the open bottom just like a metal collapsible tube, and the open end is pinched shut and sealed. The method of sealing merits some description since it also has other applications. The edges are clamped together with a small amount of material extending above the clamp. A gas flame is then applied to the protruding edges, melting them together. Electric radiant heaters can also be used.

These tubes can also be used as powder boxes or as bottles by sealing a disc into the end of the tube instead of flattening it out. This disc may be of polyethylene or of metal. The flat-bottomed ones find wide use as dispensing containers for powder. When the proper spout is used a squeeze will dispense a fine cloud of powder. They are also used for liquid detergents, as easily controlled amounts can be dispensed by squeezing.

The polyethylene collapsible tube has one advantage over the metal tube, besides the obvious one of chemical inertness. When the contents is used, the tube tends to spring back, drawing the last drop back in, leaving the opening dry and clean for replacement of the closure. Also, since it is not rolled up as it is used, any trade mark or identification remains clearly legible for the entire life of the tube.

A modified blow-molding technique is used to make a line of drums and drum liners useful for the shipment of corrosive liquids, or liquids damaged by contact with metals. (Figure 8-9)

Figure 8–9. Polyethylene drums and drum liners.
(*Courtesy Delaware Barrel & Drum Co.*)

An interesting chart (Table 8-1) has been prepared by the Delaware Barrel and Drum Company which compares the cost of using these drums for a specific problem involving a shipment of acid. In this particular case it shows that the 53-gallon polyethylene-lined drum gives the lightest gross

TABLE 8–1. PRESENTING A PROBLEM SHOWING WHY POLYETHYLENE DRUMS ARE CHEAPER

1. SUBJECT: To Pack and Distribute 5300 Gallons of Acid.
2. CONTAINERS: Must be Acid Resistant; must be Returnable, must be ICC Approved. Must be Leak Proof and Tough.
3. PROBLEM: To secure cheapest and most practical unit for investment, shipping and possible customer deposit charges.

- 5300 GALLONS OF ACID WILL USE -

*Liquid Volume

*SIZE	13 Gal.	13 Gal.	13 Gal.	55 Gal.	55 Gal.	55 Gal.	53	29	14	5
	Glass Carboys	Poly Carboys	Rubber Drums	Alum. Drums	Stainless Drum	Rubber Lined Hackneys	Poly Drum	Poly Drum	Poly Drum	Poly Drum
NUMBER	408	408	408	97	97	97	103	189	378	1060
MTY GROSS WEIGHT	28,560	11,803	13,838	8,342	9,215	9,991	6,180	7,560	7,938	7,420
MTY TARE WEIGHT	70#	29#	34#	86#	90#	103#	60#	40#	21#	7#
RETURN FREIGHT RATE	1	1	2	3	3	3	3	3	3	3
BREAKABLE	Yes	No	No	No	No	No	No	No	No	No
COST PER UNIT	$13.10	$19.95	$29.00	$88.08	$88.35	$79.50	$24.00	$19.99	$13.94	$4.06
TOTAL $ INVESTMENT	$5,344.80	$8,139.60	$11,832.00	$8,643.76	$8,670.95	$7,711.50	$2,472.00	$3,778.11	$5,279.32	$4,303.60
COST PER GAL. INITAL INVESTMENT	.96¢	$1.48	$2.15	$1.57	$1.58	$1.40	.45¢	.69¢	.96¢	.78¢
PALLETIZE	Possible	Possible	Yes	Yes	Yes	Yes	Yes	Yes	Yes	Yes
SWING TEST	Yes	No	No	No	No	No	No	No	No	No
CUBIC FOOT DISPLACEMENT	3.9	4.3	3.7	14.5	12.8	11.3	11.7	6.3	3.3	1.5
OPENINGS	1	1	1	2	2	2	2	2	2	1
LEAST NUMBER OF CONTAINER	5	5	5	1	1	1	2	3	4	6
LIGHTEST GROSS WGT.	10	8	9	5	6	7	1	3	4	2
CHEAPEST TO RETURN	10	9	8	5	6	7	1	3	4	2
CHEAPEST BULK UNIT	4	6	9	7	8	5	1	2	4	3
LOWEST CAPITAL EXPENDITURE	5	7	10	8	9	6	1	2	4	3

The above figures are averages.

(Courtesy Delaware Barrel & Drum Co., Inc.)

weight, the cheapest return freight, and requires the lowest capital expenditure of the containers considered. While such a favorable result will not always be obtained it is evident that these drums have excellent possibilities.

Vacuum-formed Pieces

Vacuum-formed polyethylene pieces have their largest application in food packaging. They are used where more support is required than is possible in a bag or wrapping. The usual technique is to form the container in the shape of a shallow tray, fill it and cover the top with a film of polyethylene or polyethylene-cellophane laminate. The cover may be heat-sealed on, or held on by means of a pressure-sensitive adhesive. Cut chicken, small cuts of meat, fish fillets and many other items are packaged in this manner.

Perhaps the most startling container of this type is the "naked egg" package developed by Cornell University Agricultural Marketing Division, in which shelled eggs are placed in a tray and sealed. The egg keeps better, the shipping problem is eliminated, the egg is available for easy inspection, and it is easier to use than in a shell. It can be boiled and served in the container or the end of the container can be snipped off and the egg poured out. There is less danger of dropping the egg and getting shell in the food.

The use of vacuum-formed advertising signs, lighting diffusers, display fixtures, etc., is still small, but the field is growing. Polyethylene can be drawn very deeply and a whole liner for a small refrigerator has been made experimentally.

Miscellaneous Techniques

All types of metal pieces can be coated by dipping them in powdered polyethylene when hot to make them corrosion resistant. Polyethylene flame spraying or liquid spraying is also used for lining drums and tank cars. A great deal of development work has been done on the protection of underwater marine components with sprayed polyethylene. Unlike smaller articles, it is impossible to heat the metal surface enough to get adhesion as a result of which complex systems of adhesive layers are required.

Polyethylene sheet welding is perhaps the most versatile of all polyethylene fabricating techniques. Many articles presently injection molded, like buckets and pans, were first made of polyethylene by welding. Typical large fabrications made in this manner are acid or chemical tank liners, fume hoods and duct work for corrosive fumes, small stacks or liners for larger stacks.

Blowers have also been fabricated of polyethylene in this same manner. The smaller ones are made entirely of polyethylene and the larger ones are reinforced with metal. Large-size pipe installations and complex pipe construction like headers, distributors, etc., are often assembled by welding. Valves, petcocks, movable joints, etc., are made by a combination of welding and machining operations. Experimental models, one of a kind, or small production items of all kinds are made by this technique.

Polyethylene as a Fuel

So much emphasis has been put on the resistance of polyethylene to chemical reactions that it may come as a surprise to find that it has been used as one component of a rocket fuel. Considerable work has been done on a system using 90 per cent hydrogen peroxide as an oxidizer and polyethylene as the solid fuel for rockets. The peroxide is decomposed catalytically and brought into contact with the polyethylene which, by combustion, increases the energy and weight of the reaction products. The system is simple. It has good theoretical impulse, high average density and a safety and performance feature unattainable with liquid monopropellants. Explosions on startup can be prevented by careful design. There is the possibility of throttling by means of a single valve on the peroxide line. The ease of making and handling the polyethylene fuel charge is a real advantage as is its easy availability and inexpensiveness.

9. FUTURE PROSPECTS FOR POLYETHYLENE APPLICATIONS

There are a great many phases to any discussion of the future prospects of polyethylene. One classification could be as follows:

(1) Growth of the industry.
(2) Development of the material.
(3) Development of manufacturing techniques.
(4) New markets.

These are evidently closely inter-related but its future will be discussed under these headings for the sake of clarity.

Growth of the Industry

Excellent summaries of the future prospects of polyethylene appear regularly in the plastics publications, and it is almost inevitable that I have leaned heavily on these for my information.

A prediction in a magazine has a great advantage over one in a book—the author can be sure that only a small percentage of his readers will have occasion to review it very long after it was made. A prediction in a book, on the other hand, must be prepared further in advance and will inevitably be read years after it was made; it thus has a much greater chance of appearing ridiculous in view of subsequent developments.

Looking back on years of plastic prognostications leads to the conclusion that there is much more danger of appearing ridiculous through conservatism than from predicting too great a progress. Materials have a way of persisting long after they have been dismissed as "obsolete," and frequently they even gain substantially. New materials can change almost overnight from an insignificant specialty to a large-volume product.

The unanimity of opinion regarding the future growth potential of polyethylene is almost frightening. Apparently no one can see any quick reduction of its meteoric rise. Any prediction of the growth of an industry must be predicated upon certain assumptions regarding the growth of the economy. Sometimes a given material may be stimulated by a weakness in the general economy. Cellophane, for instance, benefited from the great need for sales stimulants during the depression. In this respect many applications of polyethylene can be considered as almost "recession proof" since any drop in retail sales would stimulate a demand for more readily saleable packages made of polyethylene.

In spite of this, the predictions offered here are based on the assumption that the nation's economy is in an expanding state and will continue to expand roughly at the 3 per cent a year experienced over the past eleven years.

The expansion of the plastics industry in recent years has regularly exceeded that of the economy as a whole. In spite of a number of rather stable components that expanded years ago, but which now hardly grow faster than the general economy, the growth of plastics as a whole continues to be exceptional. This rapid growth is largely due to the continuous appearance of new and improved materials which enjoy a meteoric rise for a short time following their introduction. Polyethylene is the newest and most spectacular of these and any prognosis of its future, based on recent statistics, would lead to astronomical figures. One much discussed prediction that appears to have a good chance at the moment is that polyethylene will be the first "billion pound" plastic. It will have a close race with vinyl chloride which has a considerable poundage head start but which has recently had a less spectacular rate of increase. The two materials compete in many fields and the price policies of the various producers may have a great influence on how this competition comes out. In Europe, where the prices of vinyl chloride are much cheaper compared to those for polyethylene, than in the United States, certain major markets such as pipe are shared by a substantial quantity of vinyl. In Europe the development of extruded rigid vinyl film for packaging is also well advanced and the resulting material is price competitive with polyethylene film. The development of a similar price structure in the United States could easily decrease the sale of polyethylene and stimulate that of vinyl.

An interesting analysis was recently made breaking down the increases in various categories that would be necessary if this billion pound mark is to be reached.* Instead of projecting trends directly, a study was made to allocate increases in accordance with potentialities. Various resin manufacturers have also made estimates differing somewhat from this. These estimates have been combined in Table 9-1.

The ranges show that while the breakdown differs appreciably, the final 1960 estimates check rather closely. It can be seen according to percentage increases that this is a rather conservative goal. Only a few of the smaller categories would have to show a greater rate of increase between 1956 and 1960 than they showed between 1953 and 1956. These categories were deliberately chosen because the potential market appeared to exist there.

It is true that a constant percentage increase becomes more

**Modern Plastics*, January 1957.

TABLE 9–1. ESTIMATED POLYETHYLENE CONSUMPTION BY USE*
(millions of pounds)

Year	Film	Coating	Molding	Pipe	Bottles	Electrical	Misc. and Export	Total
1953	45	15	21-45	18-25	6	32-35	10	137-161
1954	70	20	34-35	22-30	7	29-35	25-30	207-227
1955	125-115	30	60	26-45	9-10	45	65	350-380
1956	155-150	35	75-80	30-55	12-15	60	145	507-545
1957	185	45	110	65	20	75	150	655
1958	220	60	145	75	28	90	135	753
1959	270	75	170	85	35	105	110	850
1960	330	90	185-200	100-110	45	125-190	50-100	990-1,000

* Includes reprocessed material, mainly for pipe with some in the molding and electrical markets.

difficult to maintain as the base figure rises, but there is no reason to feel that a slackening of the expansion pace is in prospect very soon. Certain elements of the polyethylene processing industry which are under financial pressure have been considered in the analysis. Certainly the manufacturer of small bag tubing is not in an enviable position. Competition and the tendency toward thinner bags have reduced his profit margin at one end and his production rate at the other. While these firms are in general extremely busy, the business is not profitable enough to justify any great expansion. Since polyethylene bags for packaging are competitive with many alternative materials, a price rise would hardly be compatible with continued expansion. It appears likely that any expansion is dependent upon technological developments that will make possible more economical production of small and thin tubing. There are a number of new patents in this field, and a great deal of work is being done that has not yet been disclosed.

However, expansion of the film industry is not entirely dependent on the small bag. The real expansion will be in fields using wide tube and film for agricultural, construction, and allied uses. These can easily use more film than the present entire film market. Thus, the 1960 goal could be realized without any growth in the present uses of small bags.

The coatings industry is in a different situation than the film industry. It is largely in the hands of firms whose main business lies elsewhere. The capacity of coating machines already installed greatly exceeds actual production, and there is no problem of capital for expansion. Thus the problem of increasing the markets for polyethylene coated materials is in the hands of experienced and competent marketing organizations. In this field, as in all others, there are certain potential markets where a single market could easily exceed the entire present consumption. The conspicuous one is the polyethylene coated paper container for liquids. Containers for fresh milk alone could use more polyethylene than is now necessary for all coatings.

The growth of polyethylene injection molding is the first category where competition between plastics, rather than with materials outside the plastics industry, is a major factor. A great deal of the growth of polyethylene has been at the expense of polystyrene, especially in housewares. In some cases even the same molds were used. However, these uses are being pushed into the background by the growth of large moldings for applications never before open to plastics.

The high-density polyethylenes may continue to penetrate the polystyrene markets, but the large, "big price tag" items are the ones that will really expand.

The projected rate of growth for polyethylene pipe is extremely conservative. The factors responsible for this are mainly that it is not anticipated that the chief obstacles will be eliminated in the immediate future. Polyethylene pipe is excluded from one of the largest uses, that of domestic plumbing, by legal codes written before polyethylene was even imagined. These codes will be revised but not by 1960. This limits polyethylene pipe to farm and industrial uses, but when the legal hurdles are overcome there is every reason to believe that metal pipe will be largely replaced for domestic plumbing. The high-density materials show heat resistance entirely adequate for hot-water lines, and even present day polyethylene pipe is both cheaper to install and more durable than any substitute. This industry is in the process of passing from the hands of plastic specialists into the hands of large corporations now making metal pipes, thus assuring adequate capital for expansion and promotion by enormous sales organizations.

The growth of the polyethylene bottle has been disappointing to many observers, but recent suits relating to patents have cleared several legal questions, resulting in many new producers entering into the picture. This will increase competition, reduce prices, and broaden the markets. More efficient bottle-blowing machinery has also been developed and some of the new polyethylene resins show particular promise.

It is interesting to note that the wire industry, which has had the slowest growth recently, is subject to the greatest variation in estimates in 1960. The reason for this is that the timing of the expansion in this field is somewhat in doubt. Present uses are mostly for high-frequency cable. These will expand gradually with radar and television, but the real growth is dependent upon the expansion of polyethylene into telephone and electric power insulation. It appears certain that the telephone cable revolution is imminent, and that pulp or paper insulated wire in lead-sheathed cable will be a thing of the past before 1960, with polyethylene being used for both insulation and sheathing. The use of polyethylene for power cable, line wire, and building wire, however, represents a much larger market that may or may not be substantially penetrated by 1960. Unless vinyl prices are cut further, without a corresponding reduction in polyethylene prices, a large volume of polyethylene will be used.

It is estimated that the miscellaneous uses and export market of polyethylene will decline over the next few years. The large export market will probably drop off rapidly as foreign production increases.

The confidence that the industry has in the future growth of polyethylene is shown by the resin production capacity installed and projected. Using only announced capacities, and making no provision for the fact that most facilities can produce well in excess of these, the figures shown in Table 9-2 have been calculated for the next few years as of June 1.

A comparison with Table 9-1 shows that from a fairly

close balance between capacity and consumption in 1956 a considerable capacity in excess of consumption will probably exist in the next few years. This excess capacity will certainly bring pressure on the price, and stimulate marketing activities, which may well increase consumption to higher levels than can be predicted at present.

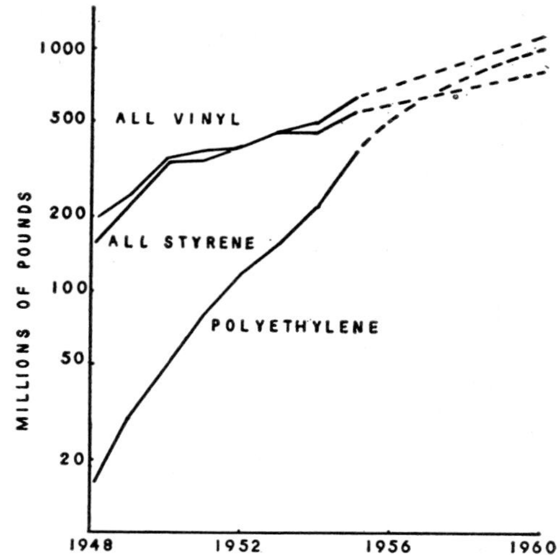

Figure 9–1. Growth curve showing vinyl, styrene and polyethylene resins projected to 1960.

The inter-relationships between polystyrene, polyvinylchloride and polyethylene are significant. The rise of polyethylene to a position which challenges the volume leaders in the industry has been recounted in Chapter 1. We now want to carry this a step farther and discuss what will happen in the future. Figure 9-1 shows the growth of these three materials projected to 1960. Vinyl and styrene appear to have maintained a steady but moderate growth since 1950.

It is not difficult to project this growth assuming no major changes. Polyethylene, on the other hand, has enjoyed a growth that cannot be expected to retain its first momentum.

TABLE 9–2. RESIN PRODUCTION CAPACITY
(millions of pounds)

Year	High Pressure	Low Pressure	Total
1956	586	5	591
1957	721	165	886
1958	771	380	1,151

It has, therefore, been assumed in Figure 9-1 that, after passing styrene in the next year, it will level off to a steady growth pattern not much different from other major factors in the thermoplastic field. The assumption made in Figure 9-1, that it will do this at a volume comparable to vinyl, is probably conservative. It is more probable that it will exceed vinyl before reaching this equilibrium growth rate, but perhaps not before 1960.

Development of Polyethylene as a Material

After more than ten years during which polyethylene has changed very little from the original ICI polymer, it has entered a period of very rapid change. Means have been found to control most of the technically significant properties of polyethylene, but their potentialities have not even been explored. It is to be expected that during the next decade it will become possible to "tailor-make" polyethylene to almost any conceivable requirements.

Leaders in the field of high polymer chemistry believe that we are approaching an entirely new level in our ability to control the structure of ethylene polymers. These limitations, considered basic to the nature of the material, are now obsolete and it will be many years before we know where the possibilities of the new methods will lead us.

One almost limitless avenue for improvement is in the production of copolymers. The production of polypropylene by catalysts of the Ziegler type is a commercial operation. It is possible to make copolymers of ethylene and propylene, or of ethylene and almost any compound containing ethylenic unsaturation in an appropriate position, by any of the low-pressure methods. It is even possible to make a limited range of copolymers by the high-pressure method.

This permits the introduction of modifying atoms or structures into the polyethylene chain almost at will. The practical effect of these structural modifications is not known in any great detail at present but it promises a new development in polymer chemistry that will dwarf anything we have ever known.

Synthetic resins are passing from a stage where simple monomers were reacted to form plastic molecules by simple and relatively uncontrolled chain reactions. This produced valuable materials, but they were essentially the natural product of the reaction, and were controlled only to a small extent. The new techniques now coming into use permit detailed control of every step in the growth of the molecule. As the smallest, and hence the most versatile of the building blocks available for this purpose, ethylene will certainly play a large part in this development, and the radical new polymers that will be produced will certainly contain many consisting mostly of ethylene. They will therefore be at least modified polyethylene although most of them would probably be difficult to recognize as such.

At the present time one important class of the new polymers is discussed under the general term "low-pressure polyethylene," and for purposes of discussion it will be assumed that the properties of the low-pressure polyethylene will resemble those of the polymers that have been available for sampling. Radically new materials may be available later, but for the next five years this is the most reasonable assumption.

Table 9-3 has been prepared estimating the percentage of the polyethylene consumed, that will have been made by one of the low-pressure processes in each of the next five years, by the use-categories previously listed.

TABLE 9–3. PERCENTAGE OF LOW-PRESSURE POLYETHYLENE

Year	Sheet	Coatings	Molding	Pipe	Bottles	Elect	Misc.	Total
1956	0	0	2½%	0	0	0	7%	2%
1957	½%	5%	14%	0	5%	3%	10%	5%
1958	5%	17%	20%	7%	20%	6%	18%	12%
1959	7½%	27%	29%	11%	28%	9%	19%	16%
1960	9%	35%	35%	15%	44%	12%	20%	21%
1961	11%	40%	37%	13%	50%	14%	25%	24%

This table envisions the gradual penetration of low-pressure material into all of the use categories, but at differing rates, and to differing extents. The fact that this process will continue with a rapid increase in total consumption does not mean a decrease in the use of high-pressure polyethylene but merely that part of the estimated increase in consumption will be in the new materials.

It is possible in certain categories such as bottle blowing that the increase in high-pressure polyethylene consumption may taper off substantially in a few years, with an increase in low-pressure polyethylene, but it is not probable that this situation will extend to many uses.

It is also possible that the high-pressure process may be developed to the point where it can make polymers having the desirable properties of the low-pressure materials. If this happens, the percentages shown in Table 9-3 must be interpreted as meaning "polyethylene with properties similar to present low-pressure polyethylene."

Development of Manufacturing Techniques

In addition to the imminent developments in the polymer, we are entering a new period of development in processing techniques. The well-known arts of extrusion, injection molding and sheet forming are basically no different than they were when the first thermoplastics were devised at the turn of the century. Gradual empirically derived improvements have been made, and every once in a while a new idea has boosted output or quality. By and large, the thermoplastic processing techniques have been arts, not sciences. Independent investigators have made brilliant attempts to lay a sound scientific basis for some of these techniques, but they have had little impact on the industry.

The growth of the plastics industry has brought many large corporations into the field, and their research laboratories are beginning to lay a basis for the scientific study of polymer processing variables. Since these laboratories are able to build up the experimental foundation that was lacking to the early students who attempted to develop consistent theories of plastic processing, they are starting to achieve some results. We have already seen new concepts appear in extrusion and in injection molding, both in the form of scientific publications, and of practical devices based on scientific considerations. These have already made considerable changes in plastics technology, but most important of all they have stirred up a great deal of controversy which has challenged every familiar assumption and old idea in the industry. While we have not, as yet, made the major breakthrough in polyethylene processing that has been made in polyethylene production, the climate of opinion is such that it seems unlikely that this will be delayed very long. At this writing it appears likely that the next decade will see advances in polymer processing that will exceed in magnitude those of the past fifty years.

The previous discussion has been largely devoted to molding and extrusion. Sheet forming, which is the oldest plastics technique, antedating synthetic plastic, is still in a remarkably primitive form. This may be partly due to its basic simplicity and partly to the way in which it has been promoted. Much has been made of the ability to use low-priced machinery. Anyone who is a reasonably good mechanic can devise a workable vacuum-forming machine for a few hundred dollars, making it impossible for any firm to expand or make much money manufacturing such machines. This, in turn has prevented the development of this process to any high degree. Contrary to extrusion and injection molding which have received their impetus mainly from the material manufacturers, sheet forming is being developed most rapidly by large end users. Corporations that want formed sheet components are finding that there is no reliable independent industry that can supply them, and they are turning to their own engineering staff and production facilities.

Such developments will not generally be known to the public until some years after they have been made. It is quite probable that the next few years will see changes in sheet-forming techniques that will take them out of the "garage shop" and put them into real mass production. It is also probable that the details of these developments will not be publicly revealed for some years. This is a stage of development that the extrusion and injection molding industries passed through nearly twenty years ago, but it is one that also promises to bring great advances. The sheet-forming technique is at present on the verge of developments that will make it a major factor in processing polyethylene.

There are several polyethylene processing techniques which are rapidly increasing in importance, that might also be considered as changes in the material, since they change its basic structure and not merely its physical form. However, they are discussed under processing techniques because they are processes subsequent to the actual resin manufacture.

The principal one of these—irradiation—has been discussed previously in reference to its present small use. The ability of strong ionizing radiation to render polyethylene insoluble, infusible and resistant to creep has led many people to consider this process as important to polyethylene as vulcanization was to rubber. While this is probably not quite the case, it is true that the improvement produced, especially in heat resistance, may extend the uses of polyethylene penetration into power wire insulation. At present, the cost of irradiation is rather high because radiation produced by electrical means is expensive, and the atomic fission products that have a similar effect are not readily available in quantity. The latter, however, must be considered a temporary condition. Cheap radiation sources should soon be available from atomic power reactors.

Another technique which is capable of improving the properties of polyethylene resins still in the experimental stage, but which may prove valuable, is graft polymerization. It is essentially a method of producing copolymers which takes place after the normal polymerization. When polyethylene is placed in contact with polymerizable monomers it is capable of absorbing considerable amounts under the proper conditions. When the polyethylene swollen with the monomer is treated with ionizing radiation, the monomer polymerizes with the polyethylene producing a "graft" copolymer. Depending on the nature and amount of the monomer, considerable changes can be made in the properties of the polyethylene. The potentialities of these copolymers have not been explored but certain uses are evident. Printability and permeability, as well as stiffness and abrasion resistance can be improved and it may extend applications where these are important.

New Markets

Polyethylene is already used for such a wide variety of purposes that there are few potential markets that have not been touched upon at least briefly in terms of present applications. There are, however, a few of these where the potential market is so much greater than the current use that they must be considered as new markets.

Two of the world's most serious problems—food supply and water supply—are on the verge of major technological revolutions because of the inadequacy of current techniques. Polyethylene film may make these revolutions possible.

A great deal of work has been done recently on the problem of increasing the world's food supply, and one of the most radical and promising techniques resulting from this has been the cultivation of water suspensions of microscopic algae in transparent plastic tubes. These suspensions make much more efficient use both of land area and of sunlight than do conventional means of agriculture, and can produce carbohydrates, fats and proteins suitable for human nutrition. The labor costs of such a system of agriculture would also be extremely low since the preparation of suspension, circulation, and separation of product could take place by completely automatic processes, requiring no labor whatsoever. The objection that a mass of algae would not be acceptable food for humans except in desperate straits is purely a superficial one. The food sources of our modern industrial civilization have become increasingly remote from the consumer. The arts of food flavoring and preparation are highly advanced, and constantly improving. It is highly probable that food prepared from these algae suspensions could be made to resemble conventional foods closely enough to permit wide-scale use, provided the nutritional values were good enough.

Polyethylene tubes have been found to be suitable for this purpose. If this were to become a major method of agriculture it is evident that the quantity of film required would be almost beyond comprehension.

Further work has shown that the theoretical food production ability of familiar food plants, both from the point of view of land use and efficient conversion of sunlight is almost as great as that of the algae.

Present day farming techniques, however, do not provide growing conditions which enable the plants to approach such efficiencies, although great strides have been made by improved plant nutrition, control of plant diseases, and destruction of insects. The major factor not yet under control is weather. Polyethylene film is the first material that makes transparent roofing for very large structures feasible. The polyethylene greenhouse may easily be the precursor of completely "air-conditioned" farms, whose productivity would be so great that the cost of the structure would be insignificant.

Polyethylene may also make a major contribution to the world's water supplies. The first application in this field has already been discussed. In many areas it is impossible to construct reservoirs to save water, which may be abundant at one time and scarce at another, because the nature of the ground is such that it cannot hold water. Polyethylene film liners make it possible to construct reservoirs on any ground. In areas where temperatures are high the loss of water from reservoirs by evaporation is very serious. The fact that polyethylene is lighter than water makes it possible to float a film on the surface of a reservoir or irrigation ditch which will effectively prevent such a loss.

Even more important may be the use of film structures to obtain fresh water from sea water by solar evaporation. Small solar stills have been used for emergency drinking water in case of shipwreck. These consist essentially of a transparent cover which acts to admit sunlight and as a condenser, and a black base which absorbs the light, converts it to heat, and acts as an evaporator. Such structures covering many square miles could produce great amounts of fresh water at a low cost.

Polyethylene film also has unique properties that may help to solve the growing smog problem. It is permeable to oxygen and carbon dioxide, yet it is impermeable to the fine solid and liquid droplets that constitute smog. This means that if large residential areas near some of our big cities could be totally enclosed in polyethylene film, healthful living conditions could be maintained, no matter how bad the smog was outside.

While the cost of such a gigantic enclosure would be high, part of it could be recovered because the houses would not need to be weatherproof, and a single large air-conditioning installation serving the entire community should cost less, and operate more efficiently than a number of small units.

The development of polyethylene able to withstand boiling may bring about the replacement of the familiar metal can in many applications. The low cost, saving in weight, and convenience in opening of a polyethylene bag compared to a metal can are powerful forces in this direction.

Polyethylene also has potentialities in fields not previously touched at all. One of these is furniture. The increased rigidity of some new polyethylenes makes it entirely practical to make chairs, tables and other articles of furniture. The first polyethylene chairs have already been designed and should soon appear on the market. There can be little doubt that their durability, flexibility and easy adaptability to mass production will increase their popularity.

The use of polyethylene for major house parts is also under active investigation. Doors and door frames, window frames, flashings, moldings, sealing strips, wall coverings and many other building components offer attractive possibilities.

This brief survey of polyethylene applications has shown that polyethylene has varied uses, most of which are growing rapidly. The decreasing cost of polyethylene in the face of rising costs for almost everything else will accelerate this growth. In addition, we find that there are many new applications opening up, some closely related to present applications, but others that are entirely new. Some of these new applications relate directly to some of the most pressing problems the world is now facing, and they could use quantities of polyethylene that would make present uses appear insignificant.

INDEX